Coping with Chronic Illness

This valuable book combines psychological theories of health with the lived experience of coping with chronic health conditions, focusing on the "ill person" as an actor of their own development. It draws on perspectives from developmental and health psychology alongside the author's personal experience of chronic illness.

Bonino considers all aspects of living with illness, from issues that impact on everyday functioning such as pain and fatigue, to the rebuilding of identity through meaningful new goals and effective actions, and the development of therapeutic relationships. Psychological theories are interweaved with descriptions of lived encounters to center the experience of the person living alongside illness and provide insightful points of reference that everyone could try to use when facing the challenges of chronic disease in the course of their daily lives.

Coping with Chronic Illness is important reading for those living with chronic health conditions, as well as for healthcare professionals looking to gain awareness of the psychological issues caused by living with illness. It is also of interest for postgraduate students of health psychology.

Silvia Bonino is Professor Emeritus of Developmental Psychology in the Department of Psychology of the University of Turin (Italy), where she founded the Laboratory of Developmental Psychology. She is the author of *Nature and Culture in Intimate Partner Violence: Sex, Love and Equality* (Routledge, 2018).

D1452098

Coping with Chronic Illness

Theories, Issues and Lived Experiences

Mille fili mi legano qui
Vivere la malattia

Silvia Bonino

Routledge
Taylor & Francis Group

LONDON AND NEW YORK

First published in English 2021
by Routledge
2 Park Square, Milton Park, Abingdon, Oxon OX14 4RN

and by Routledge
52 Vanderbilt Avenue, New York, NY 10017

Routledge is an imprint of the Taylor & Francis Group, an informa business

© 2021 Silvia Bonino

Translated by Sheri Dorn Giarmoleo

Published in Italian by Laterza 2019

British Library Cataloguing-in-Publication Data
A catalogue record for this book is available from the British Library

Library of Congress Cataloging-in-Publication Data
A catalog record has been requested for this book

ISBN: 978-0-367-42153-3 (hbk)
ISBN: 978-0-367-42152-6 (pbk)
ISBN: 978-0-367-82223-1 (ebk)

Typeset in Sabon
by Newgen Publishing UK

For some time, Jul is hovering in the sky over this desolate moor, it is inexplicable, it is a daily nutrient.

It is the most valuable inheritance I have received from man ... the best part of which continues to live in me.

Etty Hillesum, *Diaries, 1941–1943*

Contents

Preface for this edition

When this book was first published in 2006, people suffering from multiple sclerosis or other chronic diseases immediately grasped its particular value. It was not a psychology or sociology book that many perhaps would never read. It was not even an autobiography, which many would have read, perhaps remaining unsatisfied, because everyone's experience is unique and unrepeatable. The book presented a completely new reflection, which brought together psychological science with my personal, painful experience of illness. In short, it was a book of science and testimony, and this constituted its uniqueness and strength. The experience of illness does not undermine theoretical reflection, making it less valid scientifically, but forces it to become concrete, to ask itself about the fallout of knowledge, which then becomes a tool not only for understanding, but also for living the challenge of chronic disease in everyday life.

For this reason, patients with multiple sclerosis, as well as other chronic diseases, were the first to respond enthusiastically to reading this book, which they felt was close to their experience: in it there were things they could identify with, finding it as a key reading in its usefulness, providing insightful indications and reference points that everyone could try to use when facing the challenges of chronic disease in the course of their daily lives. Points of reference and not recipes, because each person is asked to make the references relevant, given one current condition of their existence; points of reference they trusted because they came from a person seen as credible due to her scientific competence and because, at the same time, she lived with the condition of chronic illness.

From the reading of this book, then, a shared journey between me and the many other ill persons started, that has deepened over the years, both through isolated meetings and my continuing work of psychological support, dedicated in particular to those who have just been diagnosed with multiple sclerosis. A sharing that has permitted me to further explore the experience of illness and to verify the validity of what is proposed in this book, where specific attention is paid to the search for meaning, identity and the capacity to pursue significant objectives, along with one's illness.

As for chronic disease, the years we are living through are full of lights and shadows. On one hand, great advances in medicine and the increase in technical and specialist knowledge open up exciting prospects, which unfortunately do not always translate into a global cure for a patient as a person, who is in need of help to live daily life in the fullest way. On the other hand, the increase of chronic disease and demographic changes pose a demand for treatment which society is finding more and more difficult to respond to, consequently entrusting more and more tasks to individuals themselves and their families. In this context, families experience a condition of bewilderment and solitude, if not abandonment, further aggravating the fatigue of living every day for the rest of one's life with illness: a loss for all of society.

Talking about chronic disease is imperative now more than ever and this edition responds to this need. In addition to a revision and an update of the bibliographical references, there is a new part (VI) on the in-depth analysis of some particularly relevant topics today: the moment of diagnosis and the following times; the contradictions and urgent need for psychological support that helps to mobilize personal resources immediately in the best way possible; the course of the disease over the years of one's life cycle, posing different tasks, with varying levels of difficulty for the ill person; the specific problems of young people still living with the family and facing the transition to adult age, separating from parents; the problems that the disease poses to the children themselves, as children, when the parents are affected; the use of the Internet and virtual tools, so widespread today, considering their advantages and risks. The result is a text I hope is useful for the person living with chronic illness, and those near and dear – family and friends, also for those who work every day in health care to guarantee sick people a better life, and for anyone, in the community and in society, who wants to better understand a reality that, as citizens, affects us closely and requires everyone's collaboration.

Why this book

I wrote this book for myself, because nothing as much as writing clarifies one's thoughts, feelings and emotions. I have written this book for others, because I trust that my reflections may be useful to others too.

I owe this decision to an unknown young woman we met in September 2000 in the corridors of the hospital that houses the specialist center where I am being treated. I was waiting to speak to the doctor that day and I was happy. Because even this can happen when you are chronically ill: to be happy with the news, which for most people would sound like a sentence, that from now on you will have to give yourself an injection every day. To me that news seemed like a liberation: in front of me a new hope opened up and I was happy. I was coming out of three months of suffering in which I had tried a cure, the one commonly prescribed for my illness, which had proved fruitless for me: I hardly walked anymore and every little effort of daily life was beyond my ability. A few days earlier I received the phone call I had been anxiously awaiting. It filled me with joy as I heard the words informing me that I could stop the therapy and start a new and different one! A spot was available for "compassionate use" of a very expensive drug, at that time not yet on sale in Italy. The term "compassionate" made one think more of the sense of superiority towards a lower being than of genuine empathic participation; I later complained to the specialist, but he, with the wisdom gained over many years of work, pointed out to me realistically that unfortunately there is nothing one can do regarding the bureaucracy, and that was this terminology that allowed the hospital to dispense the drug for free, which, in the end, was the most important thing.

Even offensive terminology didn't bother me that day. I could stop the cure that had reduced me to being at death's door and begin another which was understood to have fewer side effects. Today I know better but then all my hopes were focused on that new drug. As I came out of the examining room, my hand carrying a large package filled with packs of the new drug to take home, I settled in a chair in the corridor waiting for the doctor. A young woman, also sitting waiting, spoke to me. As I have learned later, there is often a great need on the part of the sick to speak with unknown companions of misfortune who meet in the corridors and rooms of hospitals.

She asked me if I too, like her, had to abandon the usual treatment to start the daily injection; for her, however, not even the latter had worked and now she was following another treatment, very dangerous and with uncertain results, but necessary because her illness presented itself in a very aggressive form. She told me about her little girl, how her tiredness prevented her from playing with her daughter, her tremendous effort in facing everyday life, her depression that was often confused with tiredness, a vicious circle in which one sufferance increased another. As I listened to her and answered her with words of help, I realized that there were two people inside of me: on one side, I was the psychologist who listened to a woman in difficulty and answered professionally to her troubles, on the other, I was a sick person who lived every day in my skin, albeit in a different way, yet the same experience. The patient helped the psychologist to understand better and to intervene more effectively, while the psychologist helped the patient to understand better and to communicate appropriately with another person who was so familiar. All of this stunned me by making my head spin differently from my frequent dizziness. I understood at that moment that the double condition of sick and expert in psychology made me a privileged person, who had special resources to draw on in dealing with my disease and understanding its events; I also understood that I could not keep those reflections to myself, but that I should find a way to communicate them to others. Since the word, especially the written word, was rightly defined as the microcosm of consciousness, writing and sharing this in writing would have helped me and others at the same time to be more aware of our thoughts, feelings, emotions.

A long time has passed and many things have happened since that September. Disease is also this: making plans and not being able to carry them out in the desired time and ways. Because of the falls, of the suffering, of the tiredness, but also because of the arduous path that must be done to accept to speak of oneself and one's illness with sincerity and yet with sufficient detachment. Writing this book has been difficult. It would have been much easier to write a psychology book – as I have done many times in my life – on chronic disease and how to deal with it. I felt that I didn't have to do this, but to try to merge theoretical knowledge with personal experience, science and testimony, and not just for a matter of honesty. It seemed to me that only this fusion allowed us to truly examine the disease in its infinite aspects, which only the patient can know, and at the same time to go beyond one's own personal and unrepeatable experience. I have always found it unwise and self-centered to simply talk about oneself and one's experiences, as if our story were the only reference and the only yardstick to be shown to others. It is a very fashionable habit today, and not only in TV talk shows.

The readers shall judge if the strenuous attempt to which I committed myself is successful and of some use to them. Whoever she or he is, healthy or ill, they too are tied here by a thousand threads, as Etty Hillesum's phrase recalls which inspired the Italian title of the book. Sometimes these threads can be the strings that limit the path and suffocate development, but they may also be strong strings that are long and allow us to climb and grow. It is in this rich interweaving of threads that bind us to others, to culture and nature where everyone's life unfolds.

In the book I will always speak of "illness" as inclusive of one's gender. This choice is not only motivated by the need to offer an easy read, which would be impossible with the continuous use of the two forms (he, she), but also arises from the awareness that, although nothing more than being male or female structures individual identity, there is within disease the prevalence of the person in themselves, which goes beyond masculinity and femininity.

It is true that in the Western world it is possible to trace, statistically, more frequently the ways among men and even more frequently among women how each react in the face of the disease; it is also true that the disease can pose specific problems related to male and female identity, beginning with motherhood or fatherhood. However, in an articulated society like ours, these differences are intertwined with age, culture, education, wealth, affections, psychological attitudes, cognitive abilities, values, religious beliefs, in a list that could go on. Each person draws on the complex weaving of these elements in developing one's own way of dealing with the disease; their experience, which changes over time, especially in the long span of time as is that of chronic disease, is unique and unrepeatable and cannot be locked in the cages of sexual gender. Although it is often said that women are stronger, and that they react better to situations of illness, because they are more accustomed to dealing with physical suffering and dealing with body transformations, I do not think that "women" exist as a category, opposite to that of "men". Instead, we are concrete people, men and women, male and female, each with their own disease and their own ways of dealing with it and, sometimes, of succumbing to it. I therefore consider the word "sick," as well as its synonyms, of a neutral gender: everyone can attribute to them the sexual gender they prefer.

This text is divided into five parts, plus a sixth part added to the new edition. The first introduces the theoretical principles of developmental and health psychology which are relevant for dealing with the topic of chronic disease, with particular attention to the actions of the sick individual and their role as the protagonist in their own development and adaptation. The second part deals with the main issues related to being the agent of one's own development in the concreteness of everyday life marked by illness: focusing on how a life marked by illness is being addressed – giving meaning to one's life, rebuilding one's identity, being effective in one's own actions and facing the continuous presence of stress. In the third part, we examine some specific aspects of a particular psychological relevance, both emotionally and cognitively, in living the disease, such as the guilt of the patient, pain and tiredness, depression and loss, but also optimism and some thought forms such as magic and narrative. In the fourth, we consider the relationship of care, with particular attention to trust and empathy, and the problems related to therapy, its adherence and the use of alternative therapies. In the fifth part we examine some problems of the patient's life relationships: in their relationships with others, especially in their family and at work, through to their final moments.

Note: All the quotes that appear at the beginning of each part are from Etty Hillesum's diary.

Part I

It is a rather despotic attitude each time you want to remake the world instead of enjoying it the way it is.

Perhaps it is the most difficult thing …: to know how to forgive oneself for one's faults and mistakes. Above all, to know what it means to generously accept them.

Chapter I

Healthy and ill
Equal and different

A disease is defined as chronic when it is not curable but does not have an immediate mortal outcome; it can therefore last a very long time, mostly with the tendency to worsen, alternating periods of greater well-being and relapses. Chronic disease is characterized differently than acute disease, given its often gradual and subtle start, the plurality of causes, uncertainty and difficulty of diagnosis – especially in the initial stages – and lack of comprehensive care.

The growth of this type of disease in Western countries continues to increase, but in recent years it is also increasing in the countries of the world that have a low or medium income (LMICS), following the definition of the Organization for Economic Co-operation and Development (OECD). In addition to the most known chronic diseases (such as diabetes, asthma and lung diseases, heart disease, Parkinson's disease, the numerous autoimmune diseases including multiple sclerosis), others have been added which in the past were rapidly fatal, such as some types of cancer and leukemia, which are now chronic thanks to therapies. At the same time, the life expectancy of many chronic diseases has also increased, so that the sick, both at a young age and during maturity, can live many years in a particular condition, which is living but not in full health. All this creates many limitations in daily living and poses difficult problems often ignored, or not well understood and addressed, both by the patient themselves and by those who are close to them, including health services.

The experience of the chronically ill patient may seem very far from that of healthy people and therefore appear foreign. On the contrary, it is not, and not only because, as has been said, it tends to become more frequent and it can therefore happen to anyone to have a chronically ill patient among their friends or family. The experience of chronic disease has a lot to say to everyone, even to those who are not sick, because it imposes a reflection on the meaning we give to life and our actions in the world, on our way of life, on how we consider difficulties and failures, on how we look to the future. With its daily presence, chronic disease forces us to reflect on life, on its imperfections, on the conditions in which we are called to realize ourselves, on natural and environmental constraints, including social relations. This reflection should not be only for the chronically ill, so they do not succumb to the chronic illness on the psychological and social level, and consequently also physical, given the close ties of these different levels: it is very useful for all of us, because it involves the central issues of our presence in the world. The chronically ill patient can then be considered a particular witness, who through their suffering and daily difficulties provides evidence of the many individual and social contradictions in daily life, as well as the essential issues that we often avoid asking ourselves, when it is healthier to face them directly. For this reason, thinking about living with chronic disease means an active reflection on life that affects everyone, healthy and ill, young and old, able and disabled.

The first question to ask to start reflecting on chronic disease is apparently simple: how can disease and health be defined? The famous definition of the World Health Organization (WHO), which dates back to 1948, states: "Health is a state of complete physical, mental and social well-being and not the pure absence of disease or infirmity." This definition has been very much accepted and is often cited, given the authoritativeness of its source. Certainly, it had merit, in the years when health was considered in physical terms, putting an emphasis on the totality of the person proposing a broader concept of health, attentive to the well-being of the whole individual (unity of physical, psychological and social). Despite this, definition can be highly criticized for many reasons. The first is, it is so comprehensive that it escapes any translation in operational terms. In other words, how do you decide who is or is not healthy based on this definition? How many and which indicators should be used? These questions cannot find concrete answers; the consequence of this formula remains abstract and devoid of any practical value.

This definition is even more contestable because it proposes a completely unrealistic goal: no one can achieve a condition of complete physical, mental and social well-being in a stable and lasting way. If this is the definition of health, nobody can be said to be healthy, but for a few and fleeting moments of one's existence. Not even a young person, in full force and biological potential, in an optimal social and economic condition, can live a stable condition of complete well-being. Here is the most serious error of the definition of the WHO: to propose a model of perfect health, of total well-being, which ignores the limit, the defect, the imperfections, the inevitable deficiencies present in each person. Even if it was not the intention of the proponents, the myth of an unattainable perfection is thus cultivated, which inspires harmful tendencies in our society: just think of the obsessive search for beauty and the healthy utopias, on which many profit. We forget that the limits, the constraints and the insufficiencies are the normal conditions in which the existence of each one is realized, however healthy, since human life by definition is imperfect and deadly.

The utopia of physical perfection and complete well-being is based on an egocentric and omnipotent way of reasoning, characteristic of childhood, an age in which desire is confused with reality, awareness of human limits and recognition of our concrete potential are lacking. It is precisely within these constraints, major or minor according to each person, that each of us is living. The chronically ill person, whose limitations can be very great, is precisely the person who every day of his life testifies to the finiteness of the human condition.

The evidence of limits, however, exposes the patient to the risk of refusal: one can, in fact, be scared, because we remember vividly there is a condition of limitation that belongs to everyone, but with which nobody willingly confronts. Moreover, in many cases the chronically ill person is the testimony of the possibility of living even with strong physical conditions, sometimes with real disabilities, indeed demonstrating how to draw from opportunities for realization, albeit with moments of significant difficulty and imbalance. This finding can be for many a positive incentive not to get caught up in everyday difficulties that are less serious, but to transform them into opportunities for personal growth. However, for some people it can be embarrassing, as it reminds them that others, in much more difficult conditions than they may have, manage to realize themselves significantly. Furthermore, it must not be forgotten that toward those who are the victim of an illness, as more generally with a misfortune, there is a defensive tendency not to consider what has happened to them as casual. The idea of randomness appears in fact too distressing, since accepting the case means contemplating the possibility that what happened to another person could also happen to each of us. Against this worrying prospect, a defensive mechanism is mobilized which makes the victim feel responsible, or at least co-responsible, for their misfortunes, for example due to wrong behavior or wrong choices. For this reason, the attitude toward the patient is often ambivalent, and sometimes blame prevails over empathic sharing and participation in one's suffering. But this is an argument to which we will return.

Chapter 2

Beyond the myth of perfect health

The criticism of the definition of health given by the WHO has led to a new definition of health, more realistic and dynamic, in which there is no dichotomous distinction between health and disease. In this new concept, health is placed along a continuum that goes from a maximum of well-being to a maximum of suffering: each of us in the course of his life moves cyclically along this continuum, oscillating more or less between shorter and longer periods of time between each. If in acute disease this shift is large but temporary, in chronic disease it is long-lasting. Therefore, there may be different degrees of vitality and efficiency on the various physiological systems, as well as varying levels of psychic and social functioning. In this way we overcome the childish and omnipotent vision of perfect health in human beings without limits.

This conception is the result of a long process of reflection in health psychology, to which the Israeli scholar Aaron Antonovsky has made a decisive contribution. Antonovsky is known for his research on survivors in Nazi concentration camps – he defined this model as "salutogenesis." The salutogenic approach is not based on the traditional pathogenic approach – characteristic of most contemporary medicine – focusing on what makes people sick, but on what allows them to maintain or recover health, despite the biological limits and environmental risk factors. In the case of chronic disease, by definition non-curable and indeed tending to worsening, a salutogenic conception considers above all what allows people to better live their lives to the fullest, despite the limits set by the conditions of the disease.

The sick person and the healthy person are therefore not substantially different: in living both have to deal with limits and opportunities, even if they are at varying weight. How can we understand, in the light of research and psychological reflection, the affirmation that each of us has the task of living? It is clear that it is not simply a matter of vegetating or surviving, but of developing oneself in the best possible way, starting from the set of possibilities and weights that biology, personal history and the present hold for us. Developmental psychology studies show that throughout the entire human life cycle that psychological betterment is possible, therefore not limited to one's early years, adolescence or youth, as often thought. Neurophysiological studies have also confirmed this possibility of development, based on the characteristics of the human brain, in particular on its plasticity, which allows new synaptic connections to be made and new brain areas to be activated. Above all are the situations of change that constitute the greatest challenges to development throughout the life course: changes that can be normative, or common to many people – such as the birth of a child or retirement – or not expected, not common and surely unusual, such as a lottery win or an illness.

But why is everyone called to do their best within the constraints and possibilities they have? There is an intrinsic reason, linked to human nature, to its characteristics of individuality at the same time biological, psychological and social, and this reason lies in the search for a better adaptation to the surrounding world. When we speak of adaptation, we do not refer to the passive adaptation to situations, as is often understood in common language, but to the active search for an optimal relationship with reality, as biology and psychology teach us. All living organisms try to establish an adaptative relationship with the environment in which they live, that is, a balance between the organism's action on the environment and the reverse action, so as to guarantee the maximum degree of survival to self and to one's own species. Intelligence is nothing but the higher form of biological adaptation; it has reached its maximum development in the human being, gifted with thought. For the human being it is not only a matter of guaranteeing physical survival for himself and the species, but of establishing an optimal relationship through which one can live at best on a psychological and social level, and be able to achieve the maximum well-being possible.

The development of individual potential throughout the life cycle is therefore a function of an adaptive relationship with reality. And since the human person is intrinsically social, optimal psychological development does not take place outside social relationships (as in the family and in friendships) and social participation (for example through work). Individual development is therefore not, as is sometimes believed, necessarily in conflict with social development: developing oneself at the individual level also means establishing better social relationships.

What does *development* ultimately mean? The answer that psychology has given for some time, starting from the notion of development in biology, is clear: psychological development is a change that achieves a better adaptation, that is, a relationship between the person and the environment characterized by an equilibrium increasingly plastic and flexible and at the same time stable. In other words, there is development when there is not only a change in the person, in one's way of considering and facing reality, but when this change can be defined as "incremental," because it grasps greater complexity, coherence, substance and stability within the person and their relations with their environment (as happens, for example, in a child with the development of language).

In the relationship between the person and the environment, as in all dynamic systems, a process of self-organization is possible which, starting from simpler structures, allows the emergence of a more complex structure, with a higher organizational level. In this way, a more balanced relationship with the environment can be implemented, capable of dealing with any imbalances (for example, when treating a disease with a drug) and even to prevent them (like when vaccinating); at the same time there can be an optimal realization of a person. In reality, the balance between a person and his/her life environment is never perfect or static: the environment continually introduces elements of imbalance and the person can change. In both cases it is necessary to find a new adaptation. At the lower levels of psychic development, small changes in the environment are enough to alter the adaptation achieved. In a mature person, conversely, there is greater flexibility to cope, without personal imbalance even with significant changes in one's environment; for this reason, it is said that balance is more flexible and at the same time more stable.

Illness is a dramatic example of a new and unfavorable situation that disrupts life and unbalances all adaptations previously made. In order for a new adaptation to take place, development must take place, despite the greater limitations imposed by a disease. Otherwise, there will be an impoverishment of the person and a regression to more primitive behavioral modalities, with consequent physical, psychological and social discomfort. Disease introduces new and unknown situations, and forces us to abandon habitual and established behaviors; only a flexible way of dealing with these dramatic changes allows you to maintain your psychological stability, the continuity of social relationships and better physical well-being. Taking a closer look, the condition of illness is nothing but one of many challenges – full of obstacles and yet at the same time an opportunity for development, all of which present themselves in the process of one's existence. This is an enormous challenge, because it exists over time; but not for this reason is it impossible to deal with.

Chapter 3

Protagonist of one's own development

When it comes to development, it is often believed that it depends mainly on biological factors (such as a good physical constitution) or on environmental factors (such as a rich and stimulating context). It is forgotten that, from the early developmental stages, the individual plays a fundamental role in their own development through the action they exert on their surrounding reality. This differs from that of any other animal due to the specific thinking capacity of the human mind. In millions of years of evolution, the development of living beings, starting from simpler and less organized forms, has reached the human being; in it, intelligence, which as we have seen constitutes the superior form of biological adaptation also present in animals, does not just manipulate reality and respond to stimuli that affect the senses.

The human being is able to go beyond reality: we are capable of thinking, that is, of building symbols (such as those of dreams, imagination, art) and conventional signs (such as those of language and mathematics), on which we can mentally work. Through thought, the person can reflect on the world but above all on ourself, on our actions, on our condition, on our goals: in other words, we can play an active role in our own development. This role becomes more complex beginning in adolescence, in conjunction with cognitive developments specific of this age, in which formal thinking ability is gained, that is, to reason by hypothesis, to make deductions starting from theoretical premises, to perform logical operations without any reference to concrete data.

There is a broad consensus among developmental psychologists in believing that, especially starting from adolescence, an individual can be an actor of their own development. The actions of an individual are capable of directing development because they have a positive or negative effect on an individual themself, be it on a biological and psychic level, and within their environmental context. In other words, every human being through thought and action exerts a continuous influence both on their own body and on their psyche, as well as on the surrounding physical and social world. On a biological level our actions (for example, deciding to learn a foreign language or to play a musical instrument) influence the structure of our brain itself, and their effects affect others and the environment in a lasting way, even beyond the individual's life itself (for example, by passing this learning on to someone else). Even apparently trivial decisions, such as traveling, can have significant effects on a person, who can derive new physical well-being and new intellectual and social knowledge, consequently modifying their relationship with life.

Development therefore is not only the result of the interaction between individual biological characteristics and the environment, but also of the interaction between these aspects and the individual actions themselves. For this reason, development has been defined by numerous contemporary authors as "action in context," a formulation that clearly highlights the importance of an individual's work, in the course of their existence, in directing their own development. The decision to do a certain job exemplifies well this intertwining: it is the result of the dynamics between personal preferences, physical and psychological attitudes, school paths, but also possibilities, limits and demands coming from the environment, mediated by individual reflection.

The development of an individual is therefore also the result of one's intentional action oriented toward a goal, aimed at trying to coincide individual objectives and potential with the demands and opportunities at hand. Contemporary psychology is far away from a concept that relegates the individual to the irresponsible and passive role of mechanic executor of biological programs or environmental conditioning. On the contrary, as Albert Bandura has pointed out, individuals are considered not as mere reactive organisms, "products" affected by environmental events or driven by innate dispositions. They are active subjects capable of self-organization, self-regulation and reflection upon themselves, capable of exercising wide forms of control over thought processes, motivations, affections and actions. This ability allows human beings to be active architects of their development and consequently to influence the nature and course of one's existence.

It is true that in our life we all perform many actions that present a high level of automatic reactions: as a gesture that escapes us in a moment of anger, or a stereotyped response of fear in the face of an unexpected situation. These acts, however, do not exhaust the range of our actions and are not even the most frequent. Most of our actions are intentional, voluntary and subjected to personal control, although these characteristics can be of very different degrees of awareness (given for example, the ability for introspection) and physiological constraints (for example, to have headache). They are actions based on our value systems, beliefs, social norms, goals, evaluations, meanings that each of us has developed within a certain culture. These actions are implemented in order to achieve certain objectives, solve certain problems, affirming relevant values, achieving important objectives for one's identity. Whether it is getting married, going on vacation or overtaking a car, human actions therefore imply a choice and a decision: an individual acted in a certain way but could have done otherwise. This does not mean that the individual is always aware of all the elements involved in their decision. Such awareness is necessarily always partial, since a person is not able to fully represent himself or the complexity of the meanings, purposes and consequences of their actions, nor the intertwining of environmental and biological conditions that constrain one's action. There is in fact a continuous synergy between conscious and unconscious psychic activity, since even the psychic phenomena that evade awareness are essential for the creation of consciousness itself, for the self-regulation of action and the unfolding of intentionality.

Today it is clear to scholars that only a part of psychic activity reaches the level of consciousness, in a continuous flow in which what is at first conscious can later become unconscious (as in learning the automatisms necessary to guide the automobile or acceptable public behavior) and what was unconscious can become conscious (as in becoming aware of an inner conflict). It follows that conscience and unconscious operate mostly in cooperation, and not in opposition, as it has long been believed: it is common experience not to be able to solve a problem on which we are working hard, and then to find the solution almost suddenly, as in an illumination, just when we are no longer thinking about it, or even in a dream, as some scientists testify.

The goals that move actions are not necessarily rational, in the common sense of the term; in fact, an individual can give relevant meaning to an action that may appear to others to be completely irrational and therefore wrong. This is what happens, for example, to a cardiopath who performs dangerous actions for him (such as making an effort beyond his means) to show himself and others his normalcy. Furthermore, since the biological and environmental limits in which an individual moves are numerous and not all known, the action of the individual is not omnipotent – even if sometimes we still childishly tend to consider it as such. For this type of action, a product of a "constrained rationality" is subject to errors and failures, and can cause unexpected and unwanted effects. This painful experience is a stimulus to the revision of one's objectives and strategies, in search of a balanced relationship between potential and individual goals on the one hand, and environmental demands, opportunities and constraints on the other.

Chapter 4

Protagonist of one's own development in chronic disease

Chronic disease represents a great challenge to development, because it poses far greater physical limitations than those normally present in people's lives. Furthermore, living with chronic disease is not the same thing as coping with a dramatic event but one that is limited in time, such as a car accident or pneumonia. Even episodes of this type involve moments of serious crisis, in which life itself can be in danger, moments followed by convalescence and recovery, albeit with long times. In other words, acute illness is limited within a defined time and a return to normal is expected after its conclusion. This does not happen in chronic disease, which is by definition lasting because it is not curable and, often, not even treatable in its most serious symptoms. From the moment of its appearance, it entails the need to face daily, and for the rest of one's life, a condition of disability and malaise, of varying severity, which tends to worsen over time. For this reason, chronic disease requires special adaptations which, beyond the specificities of each pathology, are substantially similar: it is a matter of learning to live one's own life growing better, despite the greater limitations that the disease imposes daily on affects, in work, in social life. It is a tiring and never completed operation, because it must be continued and renewed for every day of one's life.

This arduous and continuous process of adaptation does not call into question only the cognitive aspects of the person, even if it is based on knowledge, analysis, reflections, evaluations, forecasts, projects. It is an action on one's own life in which intellect and emotion are welded strongly, in view of a difficult but not impossible adaptation. Sometimes we will work more on the body, for example through relaxation exercises, while at other times we will work more on the cognitive aspects, such as when we plan our actions in advance in a way consistent with our limits and abilities. At other times we will still face our emotions, so that they help us in the search for a better adaptation and do not alter our behavior in a harmful way. In any case, in disease as in any other human activity, cognition and emotion, thought and affections, body and mind are inseparably involved, and it is only for clarity of analysis that they are distinguished. Even in the most abstract thought there is always a spark of emotion.

As mentioned, in the development process a central role is reserved for conscious activity, since adaptation is not passive to biological or environmental conditions, but the active search, given the personal and contextual conditions, for the best possible realization. Consciousness is a privileged space for reflecting on one's own adaptation and actions, in a dynamic and not necessarily oppositional relationship between the conscious and the unconscious. The patient's reflection on his own experience, solitary or shared, can help him to become progressively aware of contents that were previously unconscious for him.

Recognizing that the action of the sick person is essential for better management of the disease and for greater individual and social well-being is an indispensable condition for the chronically ill person to achieve the best possible adaptation and development. In other words, it is a matter of recognizing that the actors of the therapeutic intervention are not only doctors and healthcare structures: the crucial actor is the patient, and this must be aware to both the patient himself and the people who take care of him. Without this awareness, the development possibilities for the patient remain entirely theoretical. In reality, doctors who work with chronic diseases know well that the patient's involvement in dealing with it every day is indispensable, and that without it we will face failure, depression, abandonment of therapy, worsening of the patient's conditions. Unfortunately, doctors often do not know how to achieve this involvement: they do not have the time or encounter obstacles and resistance in the healthcare facility, which considers the involvement of the patient as luxury or a waste of time. All those who, at a theoretical or practical level, have dealt with the treatment of chronic disease, agree in emphasizing that for the specific characteristics of this type of disease (long duration, continuous need to change habits and life behaviors, need for self-management of therapies) a relationship of close collaboration between the doctor and the healthcare staff on one hand and the patient on the other is indispensable.

In international literature there is talk of a "partnership" relationship between patient and physician, where the former is not only the custodian of the therapy but also has an educational role, while the latter is the person responsible for managing the disease in his everyday life. The therapeutic alliance is therefore realized through a relationship not of subjection, but of collaboration between partners, that is, between people who with different modalities, skills and roles work for the same purpose, which is to ensure that the patient can continue to live and develop in the best possible way even within the limits set by illness. The doctor and the medical staff will make available their knowledge and specific professional skills, while the patient will be required to pay careful attention to their conditions and commit to daily control of the disease, with all the often tiring kit of therapies, tests and changes in lifestyle habits. This lasting collaboration, like all human relationships, is not without moments of conflict and misunderstanding, favored by the objective difficulties of disease management. But precisely this picture of difficulties is the specific context in which both the patient and the healthcare personnel are committed to finding the best adaptation and development. Furthermore, given the close relationships between psyche and body, a higher psychological adaptation will also lead to a better adaptation on the physical plane. In other words, those who do not give up living and growing despite the disease are also more likely to be better physically: following the appropriate therapies, changing dangerous lifestyles, avoiding inappropriate actions, asking for help correctly, and so on. For this reason, recognizing the patient as a protagonist in their own development and adaptation in disease should not be a reality possible only in the "well-to-do" facilities, but an indispensable requirement for the good management of a disease.

Part II

I know everything, able to bear it all, always better, and together I am so sure life is beautiful, worthy of living fully with profound meaning. In spite of everything.

Never is it the external circumstances, it is always internal sentiment – depression, insecurity, and other – that give these circumstances a sad and threatening appearance.

Chapter 5

Why me?

When faced with the diagnosis of illness, as well as experiencing a misfortune or the loss of a loved one, one often asks oneself: why me? The question is certainly self-centered, but it cannot be ignored or dismissed as unthinkable: after all, it is our life that is at stake and it is therefore understandable that our first reaction refers to ourselves and our experience. We look around, we see many other people in health or with slight ailments, who appear happy and with a good future ahead of them, and our wounded identity rebels against what seems to be an absurdity and an injustice. The human mind accepts the case with difficulty and quickly tries to find an explanation and to understand the situation.

Each of us, albeit to a different extent, seeks a coherent meaning in our life, based on the belief that what happens is explainable and understandable, within a certain frame of reference in which events have their raison d'etre. Disease, with death, instead represents the disorder par excellence: it challenges, together with health and physical survival, the whole network of meanings, projects and expectations on which our life was based up to that moment, and envisages an uncertain future and weighed down by heavy limitations. For all these reasons, the disease is incomprehensible, senseless, inexplicable, unjust. Faced with the emptiness that it opens up in our life, many people, according to their beliefs and trusts, take it out on God, with destiny, with fate, with bad luck, or with themselves and with others.

I too have not escaped this question: why me? I came from difficult experiences, from a life in which I had not been spared mourning and great pain. Finding myself in adulthood faced with a diagnosis of multiple sclerosis seemed too much to me. During the first visit to the specialist center, my neurologist asked me if I was angry, knowing that this is a very common reaction to diagnosis and in the early stages of the disease, I replied that I was not only angry: I was furious. Had I not already paid, more than enough, for my tribute of suffering to existence? Wasn't I entitled, on the threshold of my maturity, to a little serenity? Why did I have to witness the destruction of my professional achievement when I was just beginning to see its results?

Over time, reflecting on the fact that each of us is called to live and develop starting from certain personal and environmental characteristics, I understood that that question was completely meaningless. Just as there are many differences of various kinds among people, so for some of them there is a difference given by the disease. Asking why we are sick makes no sense, just as it makes no sense to ask why we are male or female, why we have blue or black eyes, why we were born in Europe and not in Afghanistan, in this century and not in another, in this family and not another. All these biological and environmental conditions are our reality, they are the set of opportunities and limits with which each of us has to make his own life. Healthy or ill, able or disabled, it is with these talents and ballasts one is called upon to live and achieve the best for oneself.

Accepting the disease as one's inevitable reality takes time: it is the result of a maturation process where anger and depression fade away, even if they often do not disappear completely. These are passing moments which, although recurring, are not however the constant feeling with which a disease is faced. There is no shadow of passivity in the profound acceptance of one's illness as a given of reality, but the awareness that only starting from the recognition of one's condition it is possible to see its limits and constraints, but also the opportunities. This awareness avoids the traps of euphemisms, so frequent today, with which many deny disabilities and impairments, in the illusion that it is enough to call them "different abilities" to make them disappear. Because they do not disappear at all: their linguistic denial is a self-deception that does not allow to see clearly what personal development is still possible, with the disabilities gradually caused by the disease.

This process of acceptance is not only slow, but it can also be put into crisis several times along the life path of the chronically ill patient, which lasts over time and is full of events that often call into question an acceptance that seemed long-established. Since the disease is chronic, its acceptance changes over time, in relation to the various changes that take place in us and in the surrounding world. In illness, as is true for other painful life experiences, a definitive balance is never reached. Thus, you learn to live with pains, wounds and losses, knowing that they are part of us and that in some moments they will be able to be reactivated.

In the following pages I will examine what, in the light of the psychological sciences and my personal experience, I believe to be the most relevant aspects to be addressed in the search for the best adaptation and the best development in the disease, as well as in any other situation of existential difficulty. I will start from the apparently more abstract aspects, meaning and the reconstruction of identity – and then move on to the exercise of self-efficacy, stress and ways to deal with it. All are essential aspects, among which there is a circular relationship of mutual influence, to always be considered in close connection with the way in which a person evaluates oneself, one's life, one's presence in the world.

Chapter 6

Finding meaning

Finding a meaning in one's life is a fundamental requirement of every human being. It is not just a question of answering in the abstract what Albert Camus considered the fundamental question of philosophy, namely whether or not life is worth living, but of finding an answer in the concreteness of one's daily existence. Adolescence is the moment when, with different degrees of awareness, the person begins to ask himself about his goals, about what he intends to achieve, about the meaning of his presence in the world: meaning and action are closely connected, both related to identity. Throughout the life cycle of everyone there are moments in which the problem of finding meaning in one's own existence is particularly critical; these are all the turning points, positive and negative, as well as the great transitions, biological and social, such as the menopause or retirement. Since disease is configured as a disorder that is not only incomprehensible in itself, but which makes both the present and the future incomprehensible and therefore frightening, finding meaning in chronic disease is a demanding but necessary task, even more than in the condition of health. In chronic disease, which leaves no room for hopes of recovery, nothing seems to make more sense: the concrete ability to carry out projects, duties and roles is questioned, and to reach the goals that were deemed significant (such as being good professionals and good parents).

But what does it mean to make sense of your life? In simple words, it means finding reasons – which we consider valid, important and significant – capable of making our life worthy of being lived, reasons for whose realization it is worth fighting, from which a sense of satisfaction and fullness can be drawn. Life acquires meaning in relation to values and goals that guide our action in a sufficiently coherent and stable way. Even if we talk about "making sense" of the singular, in reality each of us refers to different meanings, and not just one, in the different areas of realization of one's identity (for example as a son, but at the same time also as parent and citizen). While referring to the same person, these meanings can also be quite different and sometimes not fully congruent.

In finding meaning in one's life and in one's actions, the cognitive aspects are closely intertwined with the affective ones: we believe something worthy of being pursued not only because we judge it abstractly right, but also because we consider it emotionally important and motivating. In this search for meaning, everyone draws on different beliefs and values within their own culture. Although it is an individual process, which belongs to the person's conscience and which can present different levels of awareness, the attribution of meaning always takes place in a certain social context, whose values we accept or reject. For this reason, the attribution of meaning is the result of a work that is both individual and social at the same time: each of us evaluates and selects what seems relevant to him during the cycle of his life, within a certain culture and the values that it offers.

Throughout human history and in various cultural systems, the basic desires for expression and self-affirmation on the one hand, and for building meaningful social relations on the other, have been expressed within systems of values and explanations of the world in many different ways; in various cultures individuals have felt fulfilled as warriors, or monks, or even merchants or parents. In a complex and varied society like the present one, it can happen that the references are very diversified: from the individualism of Western culture to oriental religions, from the cultural tradition of one's own country and to those from abroad. Consequently, even the personal attributions of meaning are subjectively very different, and the Western culture is characterized precisely by the respect for the various choices, when they are not harmful to others. It is from these attributions of meaning that individual decisions are made in one's daily life, as well as the planning of complex actions that serve to achieve significant objectives, in studies as in work and affections. As we have seen, these actions are not random, nor are they simply automatic, but instead are motivated and planned, albeit with different levels of awareness and error. Thus, for a student, the project of becoming a doctor takes concrete form in several successive choices, starting from high school to university, and its realization may encounter unexpected difficulties. In any case, one of the most negative experiences of an individual's life is that of being in situations that force him to perform actions without a personal sense.

Many people give meaning to their lives in an egocentric way: their realization, their well-being, their money, their success are the significant reasons for their existence. For many others the sense in life transcends one's own person – as is normal given the primarily social nature of the human being – and is also sought out outside oneself: in others, in love, in children, in the realization of something lasting for one's own family or for one's own country, in a job well done, in pursuing an idea, in realizing the values in which one believes. For still other people, current life acquires meaning in function of its prolongation beyond death, in an afterlife in which all imperfections will be filled, in a transcendence that goes beyond others, the world and history. In most individuals many of these aspects are intertwined; thus, it is believed that one's life is worthy of being lived thanks to the realization both of oneself and of something that goes beyond one's own person or that responds to one's religious perspective.

Believing that even with the disease it is possible to have a personal realization and development is the basis of the tiring path in which the patient finds himself having to renew, modify and redirect the meaning one gives to his life and his goals. It is an operation that does not concern only the early stages of the disease, even if the moment following the diagnosis is one of the most demanding, due to the fracture with the past (see Part VI). Given the fact that the disease lasts over time and often progresses, meanings that were found for one's existence through hard work dissolve, prompting one to seek meanings again. For this reason, the search for meaning must be renewed periodically: when the disease gets worse, when it forces you to leave your job, when it imposes new and more serious limitations on your social life, when it puts your emotional relationships in crisis, when it creates visible and severe disabilities, or, paradoxically, when there is an improvement that leads one to be deceived about a stable good future. The important thing is that everyone finds valid reasons why it is worth living one's life, despite the disease, indeed precisely within the strict limits the disease imposes, but also within those, sometimes very minimal, possibilities that it allows. Only in this way can destinations be found worthy of investment and commitment. These goals and these attributions of meaning can be very different from person to person, because individuals, their abilities, their stories, their values, their diseases are different. They must be respected and not judged with arrogance, because they are different from their own, knowing that the most evolved empathy is precisely the ability to accept behaviors, experiences and emotions that are different from what we might have in a parallel situation.

By giving meaning to our actions and our presence in the world, we can find a sense of coherence, where what happens is understandable, confrontable and represents a challenge worthy of our commitment. This sense of coherence is of great importance in the conditions of illness, as numerous studies have shown, even in people with dramatic life experiences, such as the survivors of Nazi concentration camps studied by Antonovsky. Uncertainty for the future and the impossibility of predicting, in most cases, the progress of the disease, risk being destructive for the patient, and require seeking a sense in which actions can find a significant place. In this way, even the simplest and apparently irrelevant actions, sometimes the only ones that the progress of the disease allows, may appear not trivial but rather worthy of being carried out. There may be times or stages of the disease in which even the smallest gestures of taking care of oneself on the physical plane can be extremely important, if the patient sees in those limited gestures a way to realize one's humanity at that moment. On the other hand, these same gestures may appear distressing and disheartening to an external observer, or to the patient himself at another time, when in them above all he sees a lack or a loss.

In both health and disease conditions, depression is closely connected, often in a vicious circle, to the failure to be able to make sense of one's life. Often in contemporary society one does not grasp the importance of giving meaning to one's own existence and one is surprised that the widespread good material conditions in which life takes place today, combined with the wide availability of consumer goods, are accompanied by the feeling of emptiness and failure. We forget that it is not objects that can fill life, but the significant goals, which have useful tools in the objects to achieve them. For this reason, the availability of tools, goods or stimuli is not in itself sufficient to guarantee serenity and a sense of fullness in living. In the disease, in particular, the patient can find objects such as the telephone or Internet connection without sense and attractiveness, which instead can be used with great satisfaction and commitment if seen as useful tools to achieve the significant goal of keeping in touch with other people, despite the impossibility of leaving home.

Chapter 7

Reconstructing identity

For each of us, finding meaning in one's life is not only an abstract operation, but involves living and concretely engaging in something that is subjectively rich in value and that we believe we are able to achieve, in our emotional relationships as well as in work and more generally in the community in which we live. For this reason, the theme of the "sense" we give to our life is closely connected with that of identity and self-efficacy.

Let's consider the first aspect.

Without going into the complexity of a technical language of specialized distinctions, it is useful to remember that identity is not limited to the sense of continuity and unity that everyone experiences in their own life despite the changing of the body and external situations. Identity also refers to social roles, beliefs and values, and therefore to what we are committed to giving visible meaning to our life: in this way a young person, both for oneself and for others, can be at the same time a student, a son, a partner, a volunteer, a sportsman. If on a personal level, identity is lived as a coherent composition of unity of ourselves, even when we are engaged in different roles at different times (each is always oneself both in one's professional role and in that of parent or as a son), identity appears to others as a belief and commitment in certain values and as an orientation toward a profession, a role, a realization. In short, identity refers to each of us as a person who does a certain job, who sets herself/himself certain personal goals, who has a certain attitude toward life, giving privilege to certain values. It can then be said that identity results from the dynamic interaction between an individual's needs and competences on the one hand and the demands of a particular society on the other. It should be noted that according to some scholars today – in the current social context that can be defined as "postmodern" – there is a general difficulty for an increasing number of people in structuring a stable and coherent identity, therefore there is a persistence of an uncertain and indefinite identity far beyond the period of adolescence.

The process of building an identity runs throughout the individual's life. For all, identity is rooted in emotion (as a positive self-assessment), emerges in the social relationship (first in the family and then at school, with friends, at work) and develops as a dynamic system and self-regulated throughout the life cycle. Each person manages to maintain a sense of continuity of their identity, despite the incessant changes that occur in biological and psychological life, thanks to a process of self-organization. For most people, identity is a stable but not static system, which changes over time in a discontinuous and regulated way, but without major shocks. There may be moments of particular difficulty, linked to biological modifications, psychological and social changes, such as pregnancy, the birth of a child, menopause, more generally, aging and retirement. But these are moments that most people overcome through a process of active restructuring, meaning the sense of rupture and disorientation are momentary.

Chronic disease, on the contrary, represents a strong break in our sense of identity, both physically and socially, relative to the roles of each of us. It is not, as in the case of acute illness, a transitory condition, after which one can go back to being what one was before. Chronic disease poses unexpected changes ("I was at the height of my life and I had just got married"), rapid ("suddenly one morning I could no longer walk") and lasting ("I can improve for short periods but I will never recover"). Facing these dramatic changes, the adjustments of one's own identity that each person makes throughout their life is no longer sufficient. Profound changes are required, demanding great commitment from the individual. It is a matter of regaining a sense of continuity and coherence on a psycho-physical level despite progressive inefficiencies and disabilities; restoring meaning to one's relationships with others that has been modified by the disease (with one's spouse, children, other family members), to seek achievable goals, to review the values that had guided one's life (such as success, money, work). Furthermore, given that chronic disease mostly evolves with recurring crises toward a slow and progressive worsening, this difficult restructuring must be continually repeated.

Also, in this case we are not faced with something totally different from what happens in all persons. That the process of self-organization that in most individuals takes place in a quiet way and without major shocks, except for some moments of crisis, in the chronic patient it is more demanding and must therefore be tackled with greater awareness and determination. We may think of the case, so frequent, of the patient who is no longer able to work: he or she will have to find a new identity and a new meaning for his or her life, sometimes losing an important and appreciated social role. Since the process of organizing identity is an individual and social fact at the same time, the experiences of sharing with family and people who are close to the patient, as with the health system and the social environment in a broad sense, are relevant. There is a risk that the person will end up considering only the identity of the patient as appropriate, that is, that of a person deemed socially unproductive and useless. This risk is particularly significant when the person becomes disabled and is declared disabled, with an official certification which is difficult for many patients to accept. The fear of having a negative identity is present even earlier; for this reason, some patients experience the exemption from the payment of health tests as humiliating, which seems to officially sanction their diversity. Unfortunately, the healthcare system often favors the acquisition of an "ill patient" identity: the patient exists only as a patient and not as a person in the overall sense. The behaviors that enclose the patient in this role are numerous: one does not appeal to their activity but prefer a condescending and passive attitude; no explanations are offered to them as one may be unable to understand what is happening to themselves; they are identified not by ones name but by that of their illness.

It should not be forgotten that individual development and action take place in a social context that can favor or on the contrary oppress the search for a new identity and a new meaning for one's life. In this regard, today there are numerous voluntary initiatives that can help the patient, if one wishes, to rebuild their identity as a useful person and to find a socially recognized and shared sense in one's life. In volunteer groups, the comparison with other people – such as retired people – who are equally committed to reorganizing their identity although due to events other than illness, can be of great help to the patient in finding new ways of adapting.

Chapter 8

Self-efficacy
The exercise of control

To engage in meaningful actions, each person needs to be convinced that they have the resources necessary to affront and complete such actions. For this reason, the theme of finding meaning in one's life and making it concrete in a specific identity is closely connected with that of the feeling of self-efficacy: novelties and difficulties can become significant challenges only if we believe we are able to grasp them. Prolonged illness, and especially the progressive limitations that accompany it, test continuously the feeling of self-efficacy, which in recent years has been increasingly recognized as one of the foundations of well-being and good psychic functioning. The WHO (World Health Organization) has included self-efficacy among vital "life skills," the possession of which is considered indispensable to effectively face the needs and changes of daily life, consequently adapting with greater ease. Among them, in addition to self-efficacy, there are effective communication, empathy, critical and creative thinking, management of emotions and stress. All to show once again, how there is continuity between illness and health, and how necessary adaptation skills for each person are particularly critical in the case of illness.

Self-efficacy has been defined by Albert Bandura, the scholar who has studied this concept in greater depth, such as the belief in one's ability to organize and carry out the actions necessary to adequately manage situations in order to achieve the desired results. Although self-efficacy is often defined as "knowing how to do it," it is worthy to note the emotional composition, alongside the cognitive one, which is well expressed by the term "feeling." Self-efficacy is, yes, the awareness of being able to achieve a goal by carrying out all the necessary steps, but it is also the comforting sense of security that accompanies this awareness. It differs from self-esteem, which concerns rather a general judgment on oneself, while self-efficacy concerns the perception of one's own abilities in facing and carrying out a specific task in a particular area: for example, a person can experience a good feeling of self-efficacy in his professional activity but not in his emotional relationship as a couple. Although popular, the concept of self-esteem is too comprehensive and generic, and has proved to be operationally of little use, particularly with disease. On the contrary, the reference to the feeling of self-efficacy has proven its usefulness in many fields and in particular in programs for changing habits in different diseases (such as, stopping smoking or beginning an adequate diet).

The feeling of self-efficacy is certainly not an innate predisposition or given once and for all, but a capacity for self-regulation that changes over time and is built through different types of experiences, thanks to the significant contribution of individual themselves. Within the roots of a solid feeling of self-efficacy, we find experiences of effective management, that is to say those in which we have acted consistently with our projects. In this way, we could find that we are able to plan and implement actions aimed at the set goals, also facing changing and unforeseen situations. Observing other efficient people can be a useful source: if others manage to achieve a certain goal in a certain way, we too can do it and learn from them. Persuasion also plays an important role, because it supports the person in the belief that they possess the skills necessary to complete a specific task and therefore in activating a strong and continuous commitment. This persuasion comes mostly from others, but it can also come by ourselves, through the memory of our positive realizations. In any case, this is not a generic saying of "I can do it," but a concrete analysis of the path by which it is possible to "do it." Last but not least, the sense of self-efficacy is enhanced by positive moods, which in turn are enhanced when it is high, while it can be reduced by negative states such as anxiety and depressive feelings, and in turn favoring them when it is lacking. In difficult situations, a strong conviction in its effectiveness stimulates the ability to find solutions, protecting the individual from negative and persecutory thoughts; otherwise, the negative scenarios that are mentally anticipated only increase anxiety and distort the assessment of conditions, leading to greater vulnerability and less control over external events. In case of failure, a good feeling of self-efficacy is an incentive to retry by changing the strategies used, without depression and inaction.

Among the most devastating effects of a chronic disease there is absolutely the progressive loss of the feeling of self-efficacy in the various areas of the person's life: from work to affections, from friendships to leisure. Each patient has no difficulty finding many examples in their own experience, there are many activities in which one realizes that they can no longer do what they used to be able to do. The risk of falling into a vicious circle of feelings of ineffectiveness on the one hand, and anger and depression on the other is very high. Precisely for this reason, numerous studies and experiences have been carried out on the feeling of self-efficacy of the patient, both in the areas affected by the disease and in those that are still intact. On the one hand, the patient and those around them must avoid asking for a commitment in activities in which failure is probable, because this negative experience would further undermine the already fragile feeling of being able to face situations. On the other hand, however, it is also necessary to avoid the frequent self-limitation of the objectives and activities, which the patient uses for defensive reasons. This covers both the areas affected by the disease, where in reality having different and more limited realizations is still possible, and the unaffected areas – often by a generalized subjective feeling of ineffectiveness, in fact not justified where instead new spaces of realization could be found, capable of compensating for those lost.

In my experience, the promotion of the feeling of self-efficacy in the different situations faced in daily life should be a priority both for the patient and for those who care for them, from family members to the health facility. In fact, it is a question of concretely realizing an effective adaptation and development, of which we spoke earlier, starting from the lucid and dispassionate analysis of the limits imposed by the disease, but also of the opportunities that remain. The first step therefore consists in asking oneself, without bluffing with oneself, what one's own abilities and limits are, on the physical, emotional, cognitive and social level. It is a question of clarifying what we are still able to do and what we are no longer able to do, not in general, but with respect to specific areas of personal fulfillment and specific relevant objectives in the family, at work, in social relationships. The answers can be very different, depending on which aspect of your life you look at. This analysis can lead to reviewing one's objectives, in the event that they are no longer reachable (for example, the disease prevents us from continuing to work and we must resort to early retirement), to find other equally significant recognition on a personal level (other smaller professional activities, different interests, volunteering). In any case, there is a close link between the feeling of self-efficacy and finding meaning in one's life, since the latter translates into actions with meaning and in which we experience ourselves as sufficiently effective.

The second step, very often neglected by everyone (both healthy and ill) in daily life, consists in identifying precise methods most appropriate for achieving the objectives. This aspect is closely related to the previous one, because one cannot really identify the goals if you don't know how to achieve them. For this reason, all the experiences and interventions to motivating self-efficacy in chronically ill individuals insist on the need to choose very precise, clearly identifiable objectives, and whose concrete ways of achieving them can be identified. So not a generic "I want to fulfill myself," but "I want to succeed in that specific task that I have judged within my reach through these specific steps" (for example, taking a holiday). In fact, it is essential to identify intermediate objectives, which make it possible to achieve the final objective. The next step is to evaluate your own behavior with respect to the achievement of the objective, in order to make the appropriate adjustments. In this process of analysis, failure, from a reason for discouragement, becomes an incentive to explore ways of finding better strategies for achieving the set objectives. The importance of self-efficacy and its connection with significant, well-identified and realistic objectives is also underscored by the model of Motivational Interviewing, which aims to encourage the possibility of change in people's behavior, particularly providing useful applications in health care.

It must be underscored that all of these operations must be renewed in a recurrent and relevant way, and not only for small adjustments, in conjunction with the progression of the disease. Therefore, the psychological fatigue that the patient must undergo, especially in progressive pathologies such as multiple sclerosis, is not small in order to continually adapt one's goals and behavior to the increase of the limits set by the disease. One must accept their changing body, and certainly not for the better, to find a new adaptation in the relationship with reality, in a flexible and creative way. However difficult this may be, and therefore punctuated by moments of crisis and regression that must not discourage the patient or one's family, this operation allows one to make the most of their chances, even when they are very slight. We must not forget, in fact, that the significant actions that we perform not only reflect the image we have of ourselves, but they build and shape it; for this reason, the relationship between attribution of meaning, identity and self-efficacy are inextricably linked.

Chapter 9

Stress

The word "stress" has become widespread in common language, where it has acquired the generic meaning of strenuous and difficult experience, a source of anxiety and tension. Again, in common language, it is often reinforced how important it is to avoid stressful events, to avoid the negative effects that stress can have on physical health. From this discourse, it is possible to draw the erroneous conclusion that the only thing that can be done against stress is to avoid every possible situation that can provoke it, and that an attitude of indifference, even at the limit of slight stupidity, is the best defense from all the anxieties of life. This completely erroneous yet widespread way of considering and dealing with stress has no basis in psychology. It leaves people completely weary in the face of disease, particularly in the face of chronic disease. In this case, in fact, one can neither escape the disease, which is not curable and sometimes not even treatable regarding its most severe symptoms, nor can one, if not perhaps for short moments, pretend to be well: the limitations, the suffering, relapses are there recalling our condition every day.

In chronic disease the first cause of stress comes from the disease itself with its ailments, its limitations, the renunciations it imposes, the shadowing uncertainty on the future, the pain that often accompanies it, the tensions it creates in social life. Emotional reactions such as anger and despair, aroused by the disease at different times of its evolution, may in turn produce additional stressors. However, other indirect causes of stress should not be underestimated. In the first place, there are the medical checkups (such as an MRI – Magnetic Resonance Imaging) that renew the fear of the degenerative progression of disease and sometimes confirm it. In general, all medical practices and the same therapies constitute in themselves a reason for stress, as they represent an invasion of one's own body, sometimes requiring one to go to distant healthcare facilities, comparing oneself with others who are indifferent, often involving painful or at least unpleasant interventions, imposing a sense of submission to an unnatural sense of time and daily life rhythms. To all this we must add the frequent bureaucratic practices, which with their complexity and often manifest uselessness, are a cause of significant stress, easily reducible but often ignored.

Is the chronically ill person condemned to succumb to stress? The answer is certainly negative, but to understand "why" it is necessary to discuss at length what is meant by the word stress in medical and psychological literature, then allowing one to examine what are the best ways to cope with stress (the so-called coping). According to the classic definition of Hans Selye, stress can be defined as a general "adaptation syndrome," which involves the whole organism in an effort to cope with external agents of various kinds (from physical and biological stimuli to those psychological and social) that affect and endanger one. This syndrome is defined as "general" because alongside the specific effects, characteristic of each stressor, there are non-specific effects that affect the whole organism and that are substantially identical, regardless of the cause (physical, biological or psychological) that has generated the stressful condition. At first, the organism reacts with an alarm state, which aims to massively activate its resources against the enemy and restore a condition of balance and well-being as soon as possible. The general changes concern the whole organism – central nervous system, neurovegetative system, hormonal system and immune system – with a particular involvement of the hypothalamic, pituitary, adrenal axis. Due to the strong activation it entails, this response is adaptive only if it is temporary, while it becomes pathogenic if protracted over time. No organism can live long in an alarm phase nor can it tolerate a chronic state of intense activation, which is incompatible with survival. For this reason, if the stressor persists, a resistance phase develops later, also characterized by profound modifications of the whole organism. This follows, with the persistence of the harmful agent, a phase of exhaustion, where the organism, not having an infinite capacity for adaptation, enters the phase of exhaustion and death.

In reality, in everyday language, when we speak of stress we refer mainly to causes of psychological and social origin. The responses to this type of stress clearly highlight the human psychophysical unity, where psychological and biological aspects are closely connected. In fact, psychological and social stressors (such as conflicts, frustrations, difficult interpersonal relationships) give rise to physiological responses, both general (for example, activation of the organism) and specific (increase in blood pressure). Early studies mainly examined the central and peripheral biological responses and the activation of different emotional responses: anger, fear, inactivity. In this way, it was possible to demonstrate the adaptive function, in the very short period, of the profound physiological changes that accompany the emotional responses to stressful agents: preparing the body for struggle, or for flight, or even for immobility. At the same time, the risks of prolonged physiological activation and the link with psychosomatic disorders are highlighted, defined as such because they are somatic in their manifestation but psychic in their origin. Psychosomatic illnesses are in fact attributable to a prolonged and excessive negative emotional activation, which does not find expression and resolution. Sometimes it is believed that emotional expression should never be thwarted, that it is enough to give free rein to one's emotions to positively face stress; this is a superficial and distorted interpretation of scientific studies on emotion and stress.

As studies progressed, it became increasingly clear that stressors in human beings do not necessarily give rise to automatic physiological responses and undifferentiated emotions, but that the psyche of each of us mediates both the evaluation of the stressful agent and emotional responses and behavioral ones. This mediation involves the most advanced part of the brain, the neocortex, and not only the most ancient parts, which are all the more active the more primitive the emotional response is. First, it is the individual who evaluates a stressor as such; in other words, the stimulus itself does not count as much as the meaning attributed to it by everyone. Even if there are situations, such as war or natural disasters, which are a source of stress for everyone, the crucial element is given by the value (negative, neutral or positive) that the individual attributes to a certain stimulus. Even serious stimuli can be assessed differently by people (as insurmountable, confrontable or even useful) and can consequently give rise to different physical, psychological and behavioral responses. The assessment of the severity of the stressor is based both on the memory and comparison with the same or similar experiences of the past, and on an analysis of the resources currently available to cope with it. In other words, the evaluation of the stimulus is not the mere learned repetition of the past, but also depends on the analysis of the current possibilities to face it. The current emotional state is also relevant in this regard. In fact, dysphoric emotions can filter the assessment of reality, in a dangerous crescendo of negative attributions, strong biological reactions and impoverished behavioral responses. To this we must add that the human being, due to our specific cognitive characteristics, can recall traumatic experiences (such as an accident) even after they have occurred, just as we can anticipate what is not yet present (for example, anxiety about a medical exam), with the capacity to conjure stressful agents not currently present, but mentally evoked and psychologically relevant. For these reasons, those checklists of stressful agents (from divorce to moving one's home) accompanied by a supposedly objective score are considered completely worthless, often used in the past to evaluate the severity of the stress to which a person was subjected and still today re-proposed sometimes as a self-help tool. The responses of different persons to the same stressors are decidedly individualized and differentiated.

Chapter 10

Coping with stress

The individual psyche does not just evaluate the causes of stress; it can express the emotions aroused by a stressful situation in a symbolic way, through word and fantasy; even more so, one can tackle and overcome stress through a new adaptation. For this reason, in recent decades the interest of psychologists has shifted from the analysis of the stressful agent to those of the one affected by stress. Particular attention has been paid to certain closely related aspects: on the one hand the defenses against stress and the ways of coping with them, on the other the characteristics of resistance and strength of mind that allow some people not only not to be harmed by seriously stressful situations but rather to draw from them a stimulus for personal growth. In this regard, psychologists today use the term "resilience," borrowed from the study of the structure of materials, where it indicates the property of the metals undergo tests of great force to return to their initial form. In psychology this term refers not only to resistance to adversity, but also to the ability to face them with flexibility and creativity, finding new adaptations and new opportunities for development. In common language we speak of fortitude or strength of mind. Studies on this issue confirm that even in the presence of a situation of serious threat and a lasting limitation, similar to that which occurs in chronic disease, it is possible to respond without maladjustment but rather with personal development. In order for this to happen, particular attention must be paid to the strategies and methods of defense that are engaged to mobilize against a stressful situation; some of these are useful, while others can be risky and give rise to completely ineffective coping strategies in the case of chronic disease.

Without making a list of all the defense mechanisms, too long and unsuitable for the purposes of this book, it must be remembered that those strategies centered on the problem have proved useful (such as the search for information, creative solutions for overcoming and circumvention of obstacles, the identification of substitute objectives), therefore calling the cognitive processes more into question. On the contrary, emotional strategies, based above all on the uncontrolled expression of emotions and on the immediate reduction of emotional discomfort (for example, avoiding going to a medical checkup or being anesthetized with psychoactive substances, such as alcohol), have proved ineffective. Cognitive behavioral psychotherapy (CBT) is based on the observation that cognition and emotion are closely connected and that it is possible to modify emotional experiences by changing the ways of representing of oneself in relationship to one's reality; it has demonstrated itself effective in modifying mental states, inclusive of emotions and behavior. The change induced allows for an openness to new possibilities of action: a particularly important aspect in addressing illness. This approach provides access to self-efficacy, promoting the achievement of significant objectives, which give meaning to life and a new reorganization of identity.

Since stress acts not only on a psychological level but also on a physical level, relaxation techniques that allow reduction of emotional activation are not to be overlooked. By virtue of the inseparable link between mind and body, it is possible to act on the strong physiological activation aroused by an emotion, in order to reduce malaise, through voluntary exercises that act through the autonomic nervous system on breathing, on muscle tone, including blood pressure. These are techniques, such as autogenic training, which combine simple breathing exercises with visualizations of one's own body, and possibly with visualizations of relaxing and positive images. These techniques have nothing arcane and esoteric: if practiced with constancy, they are very useful to avoid the excess of emotional activation in particular anxiety-provoking situations. They contribute greatly to increasing the sense of self-efficacy in controlling one's own body, often so absent in the patient who is subjected to the whims of their disease, as well as often inevitable invasive medical practices. Again, it is a matter of connecting in a positive, functional way for adaptation, cognition and emotions.

Relaxation techniques should be taught to everyone from childhood, because they are useful tools for what was once called, with an expression now obsolete but effective, "mental hygiene." In all situations in life where emotional activation is strong, and often destructive, having an easy and always handy practice to not be overwhelmed is an opportunity that everyone should have. Once again, it is evident that the distance between the sick and the healthy person is far less than is normally believed.

Relaxation is linked to the various meditation techniques, which have also shown their effectiveness. Many cultures and many religions provide moments of meditation, of different depth, induced by different techniques and situations (yoga, prayer). The most recent studies have highlighted the neurophysiological correlates, in particular the changes in electrical activity and the activation of different areas of the brain. In meditation, not only physical relaxation, already significant in itself, is realized, but mental distance is placed from tensions and anxiety-provoking thoughts. Even with a disease this detachment allows a calmer evaluation and allows one to activate better defenses and better ways of dealing with it. Strengthening these beneficial effects can also contribute to feelings of sharing and harmony, such as those brought about by religious belonging.

Regarding defense mechanisms, humans share flight, attack and immobility with animals, extreme physical modalities that are put in place when other ways of coping with a problematic situation are not possible. But these physical modalities are certainly not the most frequent, since the human being is capable of thinking and can therefore elaborate cognitively mediated defense mechanisms. Escape can thus be realized through dream and fantasy, and the attack can be translated into verbal forms, from the still rough forms of the insult to irony and satire. The defense mechanisms are numerous and cannot be absolutely evaluated as positive or negative, as some of them present greater risks due to their primitiveness. Their positivity depends on the contingent situation and their temporality: allowing a better adaptation and individual development, given a specific moment of a person's life.

Denial, for example, is a very primitive and potentially dangerous mechanism, because it does not allow us to take note of reality, which is a necessary condition for finding suitable ways to deal with it. Despite this, in some situations it is not only frequent, but cannot even be considered pathological, provided it is transitory. Denial is widespread in the early stages of disease, especially in the face of diagnosis, when the patient clings to everything (such as improbable laboratory errors and incorrect assessments by the doctor) to believe that what is happening to them is not true. Denial can be favored by the objective uncertainty and diagnostic difficulties that often accompany many chronic diseases in their early stages (see Part VI).

Especially at the beginning of the illness, the person needs some time to internalize a truth that is difficult to accept and to restructure one's way of thinking and feeling, in order to take realistically into account the new physical conditions in which one finds oneself. The defense mechanism of denial, however, is very primitive and immature, and cannot stand for long without becoming pathological: a mentally intact person has in fact a relationship with reality that cannot allow her to deny what appears clearly, such as symptoms of the disease, its worsening, the results of the various analyzes. Furthermore, the negated reality continues to exert its influence and therefore the defense mechanism of the negation cannot lead to any adaptation over time.

Another example is given by regression, which by definition entails withdrawal, a direction which is contrary to development. Yet even this, while realizing an impoverishment of the person and a return to more primitive modalities, characteristics of a less advanced phase (for example, dedicating oneself to simpler tasks, behaving in a more childish way), can be useful if it represents a transitional pause of suspension and reassurance. Sometimes moments of regression are necessary as long as they are limited in time and depth, eventually allowing one to develop more structured, organized and adaptive ways of dealing with reality.

Even aggression, which is barren and harmful if directed against oneself, one's family, health personnel, can be channeled and shifted toward useful objectives, becoming an energy that allows you to contrast that which hinders your well-being. All sufferers know how much energy and fortitude are needed in difficult situations. It is no coincidence that in common language we often speak of the fight against disease. In this regard, I agree with the criticisms of those who warn against the warlike metaphors, who would like the patient always fighting, always combative and always on the front line, which means in practice always available to undergo often terrible uncertain therapies, without ever having doubts or resignation. This is an excessively obstinate vision of the relationship with disease, which protects those who are next to the patient from anxiety yet does not grasp the recurring need for moments of pause and withdrawal, which are not necessarily moments of failure and defeat. The same depression, which I will discuss later, under certain conditions can be considered a useful defense mechanism, because it allows you to temporarily withdraw from reality, distancing yourself from reality, giving yourself time to develop more advanced ways. Despite these reservations, there is no doubt that an active attitude is indispensable for finding adaptive defenses and progressive development.

The important thing is that over time each patient can find the defenses that best allow themselves to achieve personal development, despite the limitations set by the disease, and indeed using their limitations to the best, remembering once again that useful defense methods that focus on solving problems rather than simply expressing emotional distress are critical.

Part III

Pain always claims its place and its rights, in one form or other. What matters is the way in which it is endured, whether you are able to integrate it into your life and, at the same time, embracing life equally.

Sometimes, worries jump all over us like parasites. Okay, it is then we need to scratch ourselves a bit, perhaps becoming uglier, but it is necessary to get rid of them.

Chapter 11

It is all your fault

Placing blame on the patient is not uncommon, neither among family members, friends and acquaintances, nor among health workers or even in the patient themselves. As I have already mentioned, we all may have an ambivalent attitude toward the victims; we tend to think what has happened to them is not accidental, but on the contrary – a consequence of their behavior. In other words: "they were asking for it." This reasoning constitutes our own defense against the appalling possibility that what is happening to them may also happen to us. As I have mentioned, the human mind has difficulty accepting the idea of randomness and tries to find an order in what is happening, to find an explanation for dramatic or even unusual events: the attribution of responsibility to the patient is part of this attempt. It is therefore a primitive reasoning, which is used in self-defense, within what has been called the "utopia of the just world." It is the childish belief, which can be evident even in adults, that things in the world always go according to a rule of justice and that those who are victims of unexplained events are actually somehow, someway responsible for them.

These ways of reasoning and defending oneself often lead to distorting epidemiological results. It is true that there are people who have harmful lifestyles (such as poor nutrition) or risky behaviors (such as the habit of smoking), universally known as important contributing factors in the onset of certain diseases. These types of behavior certainly increase the likelihood of developing certain pathologies, but it is a question of probability, not of linear causality. No one can know for certain the complex intertwining of the many variables, of different origin (biological, environmental, behavioral) that led to the onset of disease in a specific person.

The blaming of the patient is certainly not a new fact; throughout history disease has often been considered a divine punishment, not only for the individual, but also for entire populations, for example in the past Europe's plague epidemic. More recently, a type of blame has become frequent which is cloaked in psychology and presents itself with scientific credentials. It is about overturning the importance given by the psychological disciplines to the psycho-physical unity of a person, meaning the centrality of the individual in wrestling with stress as well as in promoting and managing his own health. This consideration, which we have seen to be so important in activating a sick person, runs the risk of backfiring like a boomerang against the patient, when it is not well understood or is presented in a distorted way. It is not uncommon for a patient to be told, more or less explicitly, that they are ultimately the culprit of their illness, given unhealthy behavioral habits and their inability to cope with life's objective difficulties.

In a primitive and sometimes deliberately manipulative psychological disclosure, it is not uncommon to convey to the patient the message that their disease is the consequence of their own inability to master or pilot their stress and react without depression, but also without aggression, to the adversities of life. These affirmations have a devastating power over a patient, casting one into grave discomfort: a victim and at the same time guilty of the disease that has fallen from the sky upon them. I remember the anguish of a woman who had recently undergone breast cancer and was engaged in a very exhausting therapy, to which a social worker said that she should have questioned herself, her life and relationships to understand "what did you do for this illness to come upon you."

Unfortunately, the sentence testifies to a superficial distorted way of interpreting in a deterministic way very serious studies on the individual system and the relationships between mind and body, between psyche and disease. Research indicates clearly that there is an inter-relationship between mental activity, behaviors and attitudes, stress hormones and activation of the immune system. For example, it has been statistically proven that some people develop cancer more easily within the two years following a serious mourning. Psychological depression is connected to a depression of the immune system, which increases the probability of developing a tumor, but in relation to many other risk factors, both biological and environmental, in a large part this is unknown. If it can therefore be said that there is a relationship of probability, with variability in degree, between depression and cancer, it cannot be said in a deterministic way that depression causes cancer, much less that a single person has developed cancer because they are unable to cope with mourning.

Unfortunately, it is not just a few sick people that struggle and mull over their responsibility regarding the onset of their disease, wasting many resources that they could more usefully dedicate to living better in the present. One of the harmful consequences of the psychologically gratuitous explanations is to stop focusing on the past, which is completely useless since the disease is now in progress and there is no going back. This leads to feelings of guilt, brooding and depression that make it difficult to mobilize all the energies needed to live and grow in the present, despite the disease.

Depression, as we will see, is characterized precisely by an explanatory style that attributes to itself the cause of negative events, even those that are instead random and over which, in reality, no control can be exercised. This attribution increases the sense of powerlessness, which in turn exacerbates the depression. Furthermore, a defense against this type of explanation can lead the patient to refuse any personal involvement even in the present, when instead it would be appropriate to work hard to better face the condition one is experiencing. In other words, the patient rejects the idea of being able to do something to get better as a defense against the suspicion of having taken actions in the past that caused their current illness. In this way one does not act in the present, on what can truly be under one's control, hence increasing the sense of personal powerlessness. This leads to a vicious circle between guilt, a sense of helplessness, depression, inactivity, in which the possibilities of dealing with the disease in a constructive way are thwarted.

For these reasons, one should be vigilant to not impose guilt on a patient, especially when it is presented as a scientific certainty: in reality, placing guilt is scientifically unfounded and harmful. Faced with the disease, it would be good to cut it short: whatever the cause may be – nobody knows for sure – what matters is to live in the present, facing one's disease in the best way possible. One must understand clearly that the evolution of the disease is itself largely uncontrollable; otherwise the disease would be predictable and treatable. In other words: one does not heal from chronic disease by the force of goodwill, as unfortunately is sometimes said and written, but one can live one's life better with disease also thanks to goodwill, strength of mind and soul.

Chapter 12

Pain

Physical pain, whatever its origin, is always a psychological experience that belongs to the subjectivity of a person. Saying "I have a foot pain" does not just mean recording something that happens in our body as if it were an external reality (as when we observe: "there is a redness on my foot"), but it means having a psyche experience of great personal relevance. Never as in the case of pain does the psycho-physical unity of the human being show itself in its intimate union, a union that only our study models have divided by necessity but which must be recomposed at the time of treatment.

Many elements come into play in the psychological experience of pain. The first is emotion, in its negative valence. Pain, however, is not only emotion: as with any human experience, emotional, cognitive and social aspects intertwine inseparably. So, the perception of pain can be different depending on our expectations and our purposes. The athlete aiming to achieve nearing victory may not feel a pain, for example a cramping muscle, which in another moment would be intolerable. In the same way, the first time a patient can endure a very strong pain, convinced that it is transitory given one's hope of recovery; if the same pain continues to repeat itself later, the patient considers it permanent and endless, and it will seem far greater.

Social aspects are also important. The same pain, for many very different reasons, can be experienced differently, if you are alone or in the presence of other people. For example, the pain may feel milder, because we feel comforted or because our attention is distracted by the presence of others; on the contrary, that pain can be exacerbated, precisely because the attention of others is also focused on it.

In addition to the perception of pain, it is also necessary to consider how it is manifested, which is affected greatly by the presence of others. The two aspects are closely connected, because the expression of pain, as well as of an emotion in general, modifies the experience we have of it. Think for example of a child who does not cry when he falls without being seen, while "letting go" emotionally to crying if an adult consoles him; the two experiences are subjectively different. In adults, things are much more complex and diversified, in relation to the development of identity and the image of oneself that each of us wants to give in different social situations. Thus, an adult can let themselves cry if a friend comforts them, consequently experiencing a moment of relief from one's pain, but in the presence of others may not express any visible manifestation of the pain or emotion and indeed be annoyed by their interest.

It should be added that the expression of pain is regulated by cultural codes: it is almost trivial to say that in Mediterranean peoples it is generally much more open than in Northern European ones. In a varied and complex culture such as the present one, in which people with different regional, national and cultural backgrounds live together, the expression of pain can really be very different and this can cause misunderstandings, such as unjustified accusations of coldness or, on the contrary, of theatricality. All this helps us to understand that the experience of pain is deeply subjective, and also changeable in the same person; therefore, it cannot be understood except through the dynamic of relationships and dialogue. In short, we cannot bank on reliable external indicators in the measurement of pain.

The ability to feel pain when something hurts our body represents an important achievement in the course of phylogenetic development. Paradoxical as it may seem, because it is one of the most negative experiences a person can have, acute physical pain is at the service of better adaptation and, ultimately, of greater well-being. Pain indicates that we have touched something that can damage us, like the flame of a candle, or a joint has been injured and must therefore remain at rest, or even something internally in our body is not functioning well. Acute pain is therefore useful, and those who neglect it and cover it with pain relievers are wrong, without trying to understand what the true cause is and beginning to change one's habits.

The case of persistent pain is different, so frequent in many chronic diseases. In this case the pain has lost its defensive and adaptive function, and it becomes itself a disease that adds to the other symptoms and disabilities. Chronic pain can be so torturous and intolerable that life loses its appeal. It can seriously undermine people's desire to live and their ability to confront difficulties with one's strength of mind. For this reason, we cannot but once again deprecate the cultural delay, the neglect and lack of attention in which in some countries, such as Italy, the healthcare system continues to address the theme of pain and its approach to treatment, not only in chronic disease but also in many acute postoperative forms. This delay, which remains despite some commendable initiatives, has many historical causes. According to some scholars, the influence of religious ideologies that viewed pain as a form of redemption and spiritual elevation, imposed even on those who were not believers and mediated by religious personnel engaged in helping the sick, is relevant. This observation, however, concerns the past rather than the present: religious beliefs are nowadays rare in health care, while the objective refusal of pain has become a characteristic of our culture. It must also be recognized that pain has been ignored above all by professionals, such as doctors, who to a large extent do not identify with a religious approach, but rather come from rationalist positions often clearly in contrast to religious views.

The medical profession has ignored patients' pain mainly because it has given priority to objective indicators (such as temperature or blood pressure), which seemed more scientific, and has often avoided entering into a relationship with the patient's subjectivity. To understand the patient's pain, on the contrary, to enter into a relationship with a patient, to acknowledge what the patient is feeling, to listen to what they have to say about their physical condition, is imperative. For this reason, the disavowal and indifference to pain, unfortunately so common in Italian health care and hospitals, can be an indicator of the difficulties for many health workers to relate to a patient and their experience. Therefore, certain initiatives undertaken in recent times should be encouraged to simplify bureaucratic procedures and in this way favor therapy, especially at home, for pain, as well as to systematically evaluate the progress of pain throughout the day. However, we must be aware that this will not lead to significant results if it is not accompanied by a change in attitude, in the direction of greater attention to the patient and their subjectivity. Only in this way can we really give more attention to one's suffering.

In order to work with the subjectivity of a patient, detecting their experience of pain and committing oneself to their well-being, it is essential to enter into a relationship with the patient and not be afraid to welcome their experience. In order for this to happen in a way that is useful for the patient, but at the same time not dangerous for the healthcare professional, effective professional skills must be available not only on a technical level but also on a relational level. This element is too often lacking, due to inadequate training that leads healthcare workers to take refuge in indifference, sometimes masked by exaggerated expansiveness; this is a defense against contracting self-destructive emotions, which appear inevitable in the absence of the ability to mediate one's emotional sharing in a distinct and mature way. Yet studies on empathy in this regard are comforting: they tell us that it is possible to share and empathize with a patient without being overwhelmed by emotional contagion and that one can understand without being shattered by the suffering of others. It is therefore a question of working in this direction, both in basic and continuous training. Because the ability to grasp the patient's pain and to work consistently to reduce it is not a subsidiary quality that can be ignored, it is part of the professional competence that every healthcare professional must have.

Chapter 13

Fatigue

The sense of fatigue is an inseparable companion of most chronic diseases and in some of them, such as multiple sclerosis, it can be one of the main symptoms. Asthenia, as it is defined in medical language, is not the simple fatigue that all people experience after a strenuous activity and to which a good sleep and adequate rest can remedy. Instead, it is exhaustion that makes all the actions of daily life difficult, even the simplest, and this often contributes to patient isolation: one does not have the strength to go out, to meet others, to speak, to listen, to read, sometimes not even to watch television. In a society that has made efficiency its banner, patient fatigue is one of the symptoms least accepted and most misunderstood.

Based on my experience, it is not easy to help others understand this condition, who often consider it lightly ("it is spring, we are all tired") or confuse it with a lack of will ("if you put your all into it, you can do it"), when it is not an excuse to escape one's social duties and obligations ("blessed are you who have a good excuse to stay at home"). It may be useful in these cases to resort to a comparison that is understandable to others, such as the tiredness you feel when you have the flu, an illness that is part of everyone's experience. Here we understand well the difficulty that some people have in recognizing the experience of another; to make a comparison that allows one to be closer to a patient's fatigue would be helpful, particularly because the symptom of fatigue is less visible.

Often, even by healthcare professionals, fatigue is not adequately taken into account. Sometimes at the onset of a disease, commonly when a specific diagnosis has not yet been reached, exhaustion is considered, by its indeterminate nature, as an imaginary symptom, or as a somatization, or as a sign of psychological difficulty and not as a symptom of an organic disease. To disavowal the symptom of fatigue is facilitated by the fact that in many chronic diseases symptoms are not very precise and diagnostic tests are uncertain. But this is a very painful denial for the patient, who can become weary and anxious, when not listened to, recognized or understood. Personally, for a long time, before arriving at my diagnosis, I struggled with incomprehensible tiredness, swinging between feelings of guilt for what I considered was my inefficiency, efforts of great intention that were useless, combined with a sense of failure due to the limitations that fatigue imposed on me, including inconsistent psychosomatic interpretations.

Even afterwards, when a diagnosis has been made, fatigue is often confused with depression and mostly dealt with in a moralistic way, with messages such as: "It depends only on you, get busy, it is only a matter of goodwill." If it is true that a depressive state can also have fatigue as a symptom, one certainly does not engage the exhortation with the use of greater goodwill. In fact, depression is characterized precisely by a reduction in the psychic energy available to the person; therefore, the patient cannot overcome depression with appeals to goodwill, since it is precisely the energy that needs to be mobilized that is missing. In other words, reducing the ability to use willpower is a specific feature of depression.

It is also most disheartening for a patient, when he tries with enormous difficulty to face daily life despite the efforts made, to be told that it is only a "matter of goodwill": it follows that depression is often not the cause but the consequence of the failure to recognize one's own suffering. In this condition, one feels isolated and misunderstood. The primary cause of a patient interrupting therapeutic treatments is derived precisely from the inability of the health personnel to listen and take seriously what the patient communicates, respecting fatigue as well as other symptoms of the disease. In this regard, it should be remembered that no one more than the patient knows their symptoms, since they live with them in their everyday life. It is not possible for a doctor to see a patient in their daily life; for this reason, the work to be done, by the health staff, is to assist the patient to observe themselves, to report what happens in the most objective way possible, even with the aid of little diaries, aiding in understanding consistencies. Even the simplest and most modest person, if well guided and supported by a participatory listening, is able to report what happens to them in everyday life. In this way it will be possible to help the patient understand if there are also depressive components in their tiredness, and how to face them adequately.

Tiredness is often difficult to treat; it must therefore be considered as one of the limits imposed by the disease, above all by learning to live at one's own pace, trying to understand which situations increase fatigue in order to reduce and avoid them as much as possible. Tiredness prevents the patient from dedicating oneself to all the different activities of life: work, affections, free time, home care, self-care, therapies. These activities, if well planned, can however be dealt with separately: the day on which one does physiotherapy, for example, they will not do anything else, because one no longer has the strength to work or meet friends. In order not to lose important subjective aspects of one's life and identity, it is therefore necessary that a patient evaluates their energies with great clarity and decides which actions are relevant, significant and capable of giving meaning to their existence: these are the ones to engage in. The sense of accomplishment that can be drawn from some activities will thus compensate for the sense of loss that could instead be overwhelming if they only look at what they are no longer able to do.

In the case of fatigue, as for any other loss of capacity and functionality, it is first necessary to evaluate what one is capable of doing among what interests one, and then select the actions in which one succeeds at best. To optimize performance, it may be useful to practice the selected tasks, so that they can be carried out in the best and most effective way; it is also good that their planning is precise, in some cases even meticulous, so as to ensure achieving the concrete objectives identified. Selection and optimization make it possible to help compensate for other numerous deficiencies, which remain in the shadows, while they would instead be clearly visible if one persisted in taking actions that are no longer within their reach. These behavior strategies have also been suggested for the elderly, who, like the patient, find themselves having to deal with efficiency losses.

It must be underscored that with disease, self-evaluations are not definitive; instead they must always be updated. In this way, the sense of self-efficacy can be strengthened, put to the test by the unpredictability of fatigue and failure, which can make what was before possible now unattainable.

Chapter 14

Depression

As a quick check in any dictionary can confirm, there are many terms in the English language to identify a negative mood: affliction, sadness, grief, melancholy, dejection, discouragement, consternation, breakdown, unhappiness, breathlessness, desolation, despondency, demoralization, black humor, prostration, dismay, annihilation, collapse, displeasure, pessimism, disappointment, bewilderment, bitterness, pain, distrust, despair. To these I may add the Italian regional term *"magòne,"* which so well indicates the sense of choking given by a mouthful too bitter to swallow. All these words are not synonyms: they describe different moods, sometimes in a mild way, such as melancholy and sadness, sometimes in a marked way, such as despair and bewilderment. This wealth of terms, which refers to a varied palette of emotional and sentimental nuances, is now annihilated by a single label: depression. The medical language, and unfortunately also the psychological one, seems to know only this term to indicate the great variety of negative moods that the patient can experience throughout the years of the disease.

Several times I rebelled against this word which, like a steamroller, flattens and deforms, and several times I pointed out to one of the many doctors that I have encountered, that the word depression was unable to account for the variety of feelings that I was experiencing in a certain moment. In the best of cases, I have remedied an embarrassed silence, in the worst, some acid jokes about psychologists and psychology. That's why I appreciate the seriousness and depth of the specialist who keeps asking me every time, in a language that today might seem obsolete but which is instead very appropriate: "How is the morale going?"

The question of terminology is not secondary. We do not communicate our emotions only through the face and the gestural language, as animals do, but also with words. However, language is not limited to expressing our emotions; it, as the highest manifestation of consciousness, or as the "microcosm of consciousness" (according to the well-known definition of Lev Vygotsky), gives shape to emotions, molds them, modifies them. The emotion communicated in words is not the same emotion that has not yet found suitable terms to be expressed. It is an experience that we all had when we were prey to very strong emotions: when we were able to translate into words that knot that tightened our throats and twisted our stomachs, often it was very difficult – our state of being was different. It is not essential to talk to someone about it, although it may be of great help. Even to talk to yourself, even in a garbled way, allows you to give shape to the shocking sensations we experience, to let them out of the darkness of a confused and only physical experience to make them land in the consciousness of thought.

Through the word, which belongs to us but at the same time to a specific language, we can think about our emotions, and this thought builds and modifies our emotional experience. Through our internal language – the internalized form of that egocentric language that has played a large part in behavior regulation since childhood – our emotional experience is shaped, can be transformed. Being able to say to yourself "I feel a deep and powerless anger in the face of illness" is a different way of experiencing that anger, it allows you to communicate and share it with others and it is the first indispensable step for overcoming it. Giving a name to emotions is the only truly human way of living them, different from that of animals, which also have a rich emotional life. Through speech the emotions – from mainly physical experience – become symbolic, and with these symbols our mind can work, alone or together with others. For these reasons, therapeutic proposals that claim to help people cope with their emotional experiences simply by releasing emotional tension on a physical level are without foundation and efficacy.

The words we use to define an emotional state, and to share it with others, are therefore very relevant. Using the word "depression" as an all-encompassing label of any negative mood flattens the understanding of these emotional states and makes it difficult to identify them. The result is an impoverishment of the ability to understand one's own emotional experience and to communicate it, as well as the possibility of modifying it. As an antidote, this exercise could be useful: ask yourself which, among the many words of your language to define a negative mood, best suits what you are experiencing at a certain moment. We can thus discover that we are sad but not desperate, lost but not disheartened, determined to live despite the disease, but at the same time melancholy for what we have lost.

Complementary to the labeling of any negative emotional state as depression, in healthcare practice there is the more or less explicit message that depression must be absolutely avoided and, when it occurs, promptly fought with psychotropic drugs. This attitude refers to the way depression is considered today: an unacceptable and shameful evil. In a society that has made efficiency, not just physical, its myth, depression is seen as an intolerable experience, almost as a fault. The paradox is that depression is continuously increasing today, so much so that it is the dominant psychic pathology in the Western world. This is not surprising, because the two phenomena – depression and rejection of any imperfections – are closely connected. Social models point to a strongly individualistic affirmation, to the success of a self that has been defined as "maximum," to underline the high expectations and the desire for perfection, while fierce competition and the lack of significant links with the social community accentuate the sense of isolation. Added to this, according to many psychologists, the difficulty of finding a meaning in one's life that is not limited to a personal and consumer affirmation characterized by possession. But the more you aim for perfection and you seek an individualistic affirmation, the less you accept your own inescapable limits, as well as the inevitable defeats and disappointments that you face when you cultivate too high expectations. All this is answered with depression, that is to say with an egocentric and individualistic retreat on oneself, in a vicious circle that can become quite destructive.

To break this vicious circle, it would be necessary to look depression in the face, an indispensable premise for attempting a better adaptation. In concrete terms, it is critical to deal with negative feelings, to stop and understand what they mean, what message they bring us about our lives, our goals and our ways of dealing with difficulties, what suggestions can they give us on what could be changed in us and in our relationships. On the contrary, it is often preferred to hide depression in alcohol, in hyperactivity, in purchases, in excesses of various kinds. Even psychiatric drugs, which can be useful to promote greater mental openness and greater emotional serenity, thanks to which finding more creative defenses and better adaptations, risk becoming one of the many means to cover depression.

For these reasons, if the more severe form is excluded, the so-called major depression, which seems to have the main cause of its onset in biological dysfunctions, depression, in disease as well as in health, must be experienced as a moment that has something to tell us and teach us. It is therefore a matter of accepting the oscillations of our mood not only as one of the many limits of our imperfect human condition, but also as defense mechanisms useful for development, through suffering and the temporary withdrawal from action. Let us not forget that immobility, catatonia and the "death reflex" are widespread defense mechanisms throughout the animal kingdom, when action, both in the form of struggle and flight, would be too dangerous. Depression, with its baggage of negative and distorted interpretations, altered mood, passivity and physical malaise, is certainly a dangerous defensive mechanism that presents many risks, but which can also be useful if transitory and not very marked. Under these conditions, depression can become an opportunity for growth: because it allows you to see reality with lucid clarity, not to give in to self-deception and delusions of omnipotence, to withdraw for a moment from the world to think and not act immediately. In fact, it should be remembered that in mild depression, and limited to this, the person's assessments are not at all unrealistic, but rather more objective, to the point that we speak of "depressive realism." On the contrary, the evaluations of the so-called normal people, and even more of the euphoric ones, are altered in an illusory positive sense. This finding confirms that a temporary phase of mild negative mood can be useful for the patient to observe his condition with greater clarity for objectivity, and to plan actions useful for his well-being and development.

Chapter 15

Mourning and loss

The chronically ill person repeatedly experiences feelings of loss, both at the beginning of their diagnosis and with the progression of the disease; such as losses of efficiency, capacity, physical functionality, autonomy, personal and social realizations. These losses can be very serious and concern important aspects of physical function until they become real impairments; but also when professional and personal relations are affected, even if less visible, the loss is certainly not less painful. In this sense, the condition of the patient can be shared with those who have suffered lacerating losses in their life: the death of a child for a mother, the destruction of the home due to an earthquake, the abandonment of one's homeland for a refugee.

The process that leads to accepting losses, living with them and continuing to develop within the serious limits imposed by a disease is never linear and painless. The moments of suffering are many and recurrent, in the face of an incurable disease and its progressive worsening, with the onset of deprivations it entails. Often the patient faces these losses with great difficulty; early manifestations may include negating the loss or losses themselves, frequently with the use of euphemisms in an attempt to sweeten the damage caused by one's disease. As has already been said, calling the loss of the normal functionality of an organ "different ability" certainly does not help to better face the problems that a disability poses in daily life. Behind this linguistic palette lies the refusal, both personally and socially, to accept the progressive limitations imposed by a disease and the negative feelings that derive from it.

The refusal of negative feelings in the face of loss is linked to the demand (even though this may not be clear it is none the less precise) to behave in a perfect way, fully adapted and mature, without ever giving in or isolating oneself. The search for a perfect adaptation without flaws is inhuman, if we simply think of the limited nature of the human being; yet some patients become obsessed and do not forgive themselves their shortcomings, entering a vicious circle in which the pain of loss being suffered is combined with a feeling of failure of not being able to cope. Although it may be excessive to speak, as someone sometimes claims, of a patient's right to have moments of depression and negativity, certainly to the patient, as to any other person, perfection cannot be required. For this reason, the moments in which negative feelings prevail must be accepted, albeit they should not be used as an excuse, a cover for regressing rather than progressing.

In the face of the heavy losses that illness imposes, as well as before the death of a loved one, there is no need to seek total and complete pacification for a definitive overcoming, because it is humanly impossible to achieve. As I have learned the hard way, looking for this definitive resolution exposes one to the constant risk of feelings of failure, as the painstakingly achieved balances easily collapse, the loss suffered adds to the discomfort of not being able to overcome it. The sense of failure is thus added to that of loss, and the burden greatly risks being unsustainable. Over time I have understood that there are experiences of loss that cannot be completely overcome: it is asking too much of oneself and exposing oneself to recurring feelings of grave despair that prevent new growth. Serious losses are like wounds that are part of us, with which we must learn to live and from whose presence derive reason for growth, even if sometimes these wounds can reopen, hurt and bleed again.

For these reasons, I have always found the expression, used by psychologists, of "elaboration of mourning" completely unsatisfactory. On the theoretical level, the expression is certainly correct, since mourning requires a profound work of readjustment and restructuring of oneself and one's relationships with life, hardly engaging the person on a cognitive and emotional level. In current use and practice, however, the term seems to refer to a total and definitive overcoming of the loss suffered. The loss, on the contrary, is always with us, and this is clear to those who have experienced both death and disease; in the latter one can lose parts of one's body, or functionality of important organs, or significant opportunities for social participation. The loss must certainly be worked out, in the sense that its presence must be recomposed in a new framework, which is one of growth and not of stasis or involution. If one accepts this, one will not be frightened if losses that seemed to be completely overcome reappear even after a long time as burning wounds capable of making one suffer. New situations, in fact, can make intolerable privations that for a long time seemed to have lost their power to harm. If one experiences these moments as the normal re-emergence of suffering for a significant loss that can never be completely canceled, one can face them without feelings of failure, with greater ease and less waste of time and energy. The awareness that what we are experiencing will not be the last time that a shortcoming will make us suffer, and that we will have to reckon with them continuously in the course of our life, will help us find a new adaptation and a new balance.

Chapter 16

Optimism and happiness

Talking about optimism and happiness in illness can seem para-doxical and almost offensive, considering the intolerable and inhu-mane sufferings to which a patient is subjected, together with the conditions in which one is forced to live. More generally, many people, even those who are not ill, consider the current emphasis on optimism and happiness – topics that economists are also very concerned about today – as the result of a superficial attitude, unable to account for the tragedy of existence and torment of the afflicted. The term "happiness" may actually appear excessive, since it seems more applicable to a transitory condition than to a state of lasting stability; words like well-being, serenity, contentment seem to be more appropriate. These feelings too are located along a con-tinuum that goes from a condition of maximum malaise to one of maximum well-being. Whichever way you define it, it is undeniable that there is a strong aspiration of humans toward a positive state of mind and life. Even the American Declaration of Independence, as is known, has placed the pursuit of happiness among the inali-enable rights of the human person, together with those to life and freedom. I therefore believe that it is useful to reflect on these issues, relevant both for those who are sick and for those who are not, and much less banal than what certain manual proposals might suggest.

It is the opinion shared by psychologists that at the base of unhappiness there are not the misfortunes that occurred to a person as much as it is their mental attitude toward those events. In particular, depression is based on the belief that there is no pos-sibility of control and regulation over one's life and actions, accom-panied by an explanatory egocentric and negative style. The sense of failure to control, so frequent with disease, can go as far as an experience of total impotence, which has been defined as "learned impotence"; the latter leads to "giving up" believing that all action is devoid of meaning, importance and usefulness. The explanatory style concerns the way of interpreting events; with depression it is self-centered and pessimistic, and systematically reports negative events to itself and to its own incapacity, by not giving value nor positive merit when and where it is due. Many people make the initial mistake of not discriminating in which areas they can exercise their action and needlessly worry about issues over which they have no control. In this way they only increase the sense of helplessness and reinforce the tendency to report one's failures to oneself; the inclination to mull over aggravates these attitudes, in a crescendo of pessimistic evaluations, erroneous interpretations, inaction and bad adaptations.

Starting from these indications, convincing evidence has been accumulated that depression can be effectively combated if a person learns to actively change their explanatory style and one's control over reality. Cognitive therapies do just that, starting from the belief that our judgments and evaluations are much more to cause depression than our unconscious conflicts: therefore it is possible to overcome the depressive state by systematically changing one's interpretative automatism and finding a sense of effective control in our actions, first of all by selecting the areas on which it is possible to exercise it. It is that feeling of self-efficacy that we have already talked about (see Part II), which can be actively learned and rebuilt, acting gradually on specific objectives, thus tangibly consolidating one's feeling of power and know-how.

The sense of self-efficacy is the opposite of learned helplessness. It is not a question of mechanically applying simple exercises pre-packaged: in order to be such, the feeling of self-efficacy must be exercised on significant objectives, endowed with value and meaning for the person, and importantly are within the scope of his/her possibilities of control and action. In the first place, therefore, it is necessary to know how to distinguish the areas in which it is possible to act effectively, to then engage in them with effective strategies, discarding what one is not able to modify. In this regard, it should be noted that the use of pharmacological treatment, useful for releasing energy and for promoting change, proves to be counterproductive when it becomes the only way to deal with depressive feelings, as is unfortunately happening in many cases. In fact, this method of solution makes wellness depend on the drug and the doctor, without any active change in one's way of thinking. In this way, the sense of control and mastery over one's life and actions are likely to decrease and the sense of personal failure to increase.

The discovery of the importance of the ways in which we interpret reality has led some to believe that there are "positive illusions," real cognitive distortions about themselves and the assessment of their health, which would allow them to maintain optimism for the future and therefore could play a positive role. In the case of chronic disease, this optimism that does not take reality into account, and rather deforms it in its favor in a childish and egocentric way, cannot lead to constructive ways of living a situation of suffering and loss that will last forever. Over time, fruitful adaptation and development are not possible, if you do not start from the lucid recognition of the reality of the disease, with the limits that it imposes but it also offers the space for this realization. Although painful, and sometimes accompanied by moments of deep despair, this recognition is indispensable for finding new adaptations, new personal growth and new ways to fulfill oneself. In fact, it is not a question of exerting an unrealistic optimism and of cultivating easily deniable illusions, rather of engaging oneself in identifying which actions that are significant for us can be implemented, which allows one illness, to build a feeling of self-efficacy in this regard. In other words, the positive projects are those that are significant for themselves and for their identity, capable of giving meaning to their existence, and a confidence in their ability to be realized, based on the concrete knowledge of the strategies that can be used. The illusions do not allow this precise adaptation and indeed often give way to disillusionment and despair.

The expression "effective optimism," used by some authors, may be able to better define this type of positive attitude: it is a matter of looking at one's limits realistically while maintaining optimism about what we can achieve within these constraints. Once the pessimist's dark glasses are removed, the alternative will not be to put on a pair of pink glasses to pretend that everything is going to be okay. Starting from the analysis of what we can do, we must have confidence in our ability to face, today as tomorrow, the difficulties that will gradually arise. In particular, it is a matter of identifying what it is possible to act on, abandoning what is no longer within our possibilities, even if it was in the past. This process of selection is actually necessary for every person, especially with aging, but it becomes particularly urgent with disease, which poses continuous limitations, and the risk of a strong feeling of impotence. Since this process is demanding, both cognitively and emotionally, we can also speak of a "creative optimism," capable of not being entangled in the habits learned, but of modifying them and abandoning them if necessary, to find new solutions to unexpected problems that arise with disease every day.

The goal is not to achieve an idiotic and superficial optimism, which is filled with illusion and self-deception about oneself and the world. The goal is a flexible optimism, open to reality and its challenges, capable of responding creatively to difficulties, to not be closed to change, but to be open, willingly in search of new adaptations even in the most challenging situations. As we saw in the first part of this book, adaptation, being flexible, creates a more stable balance between the person and their environment. In this perspective, happiness is not a passive condition of bliss, but the result of growth and an active search for adaptation, which has more to do with inner wisdom than with external conditions of life. In the same way, hope is not foolish or groundless optimism, but creative openness to the future and its challenges, overcoming one's own self-centered point of view, a determinism that claims to know everything and foresee everything. In other words, a hope that arises from the criticism of one's evaluations, no longer considering negative forecasts for the future as finite; on the contrary, providing room for uncertainty and probability, opening up to trust one's resources and the help from others, to change and to seek new adaptations.

In concrete terms, this entails an active commitment on the part of the patient. Never as in illness is it necessary to work in order not to be overwhelmed by egocentric and distorted interpretations, by self-destructive brooding, by unmotivated fears, by paralyzing passivity. Social isolation, as well as physical limitations, negate the important weapon of social exchanges (feeling a living part of one's community and even more by helping others) to counteract negative feelings. Specifically, helping others is a powerful antidote to depression and unhappiness: disease often confines one to being the object of help than the one to provide help. This is a highly overlooked and neglected aspect, on which it is worth insisting: an ill person cannot be relegated to the identity of a person only in need, but needs to be able to continue living as a person useful to others. It will be a matter of understanding in which situations and in what ways, for the individual patient at a specific moment of their illness, can this human need to help others be exercised.

Chapter 17

Logical thought and magical thought

Chronic illness places a patient in front of great difficulties in understanding what is happening to them, particularly since the causes are unknown and the therapies uncertain. Sometimes a patient has the feeling of being faced with an insurmountable wall, where all attempts at understanding and treatment end up clashing with one another, producing questions such as "Why has there been a deterioration?" "Why hasn't the therapy worked?" "What about the future?" – questions without answers. It is common to underscore the emotional aspects of this situation, that is certainly relevant, forgetting the importance of cognitive reaction and the tight connection that exists between emotion and cognition.

To understand the complexity of the cognitive processes underlying the understanding of a disease and ways of living with it, also in its treatment, it is necessary to remember that human thought is not unitary, but presents different forms that develop and intertwine throughout the years of childhood and adolescence, also coexisting in adults. It is the general law of development that the most primitive forms of thought do not disappear completely, but continue to exist and can prevail in particular moments. The logical thinking of the adult is the arrival point of a long and slow developmental process which has its foundation in neurophysiological maturity but which is also strongly affected by culture and schooling.

Around two years of life the child becomes able to recall to mind what is not perceptually present and begins to work on these thoughts: like all parents can observe, indexing a capacity to defer an imitation to a time when the model is absent (imitating a cat's meow that was seen the day before), the symbolic game or pretend (pretending that a box is a car), understanding and the development of language (a set of sounds is used as a conventional sign that is representative of a thing or a concept), then after can be accompanied by drawing, imagination, fantastic play. However, in the young child the ability to think things and concepts is still deeply imbedded in self-centeredness and the distance from reality is minimal; they therefore believe they can act directly with their own thoughts, words and actions on reality, while their reasoning is based on perceptually relevant analogies and combinations that can give rise to reasoning errors (for example, a larger object is considered heavier). This type of thinking is capable of unusual intuitions and combinations, which can be arbitrary on a logical level but which are also the basis, throughout life, of creative thinking. The development of logical thinking involves a progressive distancing from reality, on which a child becomes able to operate logically in the period of elementary school, with the limit, however, that they still need concrete and perceptive support (for example, fractions are understood referring to a cake divided into parts).

Only in early adolescence, in relation to neurophysiological development but also to schooling, do boys and girls become able to reason in an entirely abstract way, to make hypotheses, to deduce logical consequences from purely theoretical premises. Western culture is characterized by the maximum development of logical thinking, which has found its highest expression in science; nevertheless, hypothetical-deductive thinking does not constitute the adult's only way of reasoning. It usefully coexists with intuitive thinking, which connects phenomena in a flexible and daring way, and whose creative illuminations are confronted with the rigor of logical thinking.

Logical thinking also coexists with other primitive forms of thought, such as magic, which is characteristic of a child between three and five years, the age at which it constitutes the dominant mode of adaptation and functioning. As we have just said, childish thinking does not propose distance from oneself and the surrounding world, and magism is precisely the consequence of non-differentiation and syncretism between self and reality. A child does not differentiate between himself and the external world, between subjective and objective reality, between psychic and physical, and therefore believes that there is a permeability between these two spheres (one can act on reality with thought or with the repetition of an act ritual, while external reality, like an astral configuration, can act on us). Due to the strong egocentrism, the external world, not well distinguished from the internal one, is represented according to its emotions (an environment is considered threatening if the child is afraid) when the intentional characteristics of the psychic world are attributed to the external world. The result is an animist attitude, for which things are animated and endowed with intentionality like people (for example, a closet, due to its shape, may appear ugly).

Egocentrism also gives rise to a "realistic" attitude, for which psychological phenomena, such as thought, dreaming or words, are endowed with reality and with their own action (a bad thought about someone can actually hurt that person). Since there is a relationship of participation between phenomena, these are not linked by logical cause-effect relationships, meaning everything that happens is never accidental. In magical reasoning, chance, so difficult for human thought to accept, does not exist and phenomena that in reality have no connection between them can be considered, on the contrary, in a relationship of mutual influence. The possibility of magically affecting reality is based precisely on participation: in fact, it is possible to operate on one level (the symbolic one) and act effectively on another level (the real one); it is also possible to connect phenomena between them that are distant and physically disconnected from one other.

It is not uncommon for people to resort to magical thinking in situations of illness, as well as in threatening and dangerous situations. Many are surprised that a sick person, totally rational and perhaps engaged in a job that requires scientific mentality and skills, in the face of illness may also use forms of magical thinking. Why then do educated and rational people resort to forms of magism? In order to try to answer this question and to understand the contradictions of the phenomenon, it is necessary to remember that magical thinking performs various functions. Next to a cognitive function, as a way of explaining unknown and potentially threatening events, magism also performs a defensive and propitiatory function: particularly relevant in confronting dangers, in order to protect oneself and gain the favor of positive forces, so that they can counteract negative events. Since the most primitive forms of thought do not completely disappear, magism can reappear in particular moments, when, faced with a situation that is too incomprehensible and threatening, the use of logical thinking appears to the person insufficient to respond to his or her cognitive and emotional needs. One of these moments is precisely illness, where magical thinking can manifest itself as regression to more primitive ways of thinking, in a direction that is therefore not developmental. Regression, as has been said, constitutes a frequent defense mechanism, acceptable if not too marked or lasting: when the individual cannot find satisfactory adaptation, he returns to behavior and ways of thinking and relating which are more primitive, and may use those that in the past had been adaptive, hoping to function even in the present.

Sometimes a sort of split occurs in the reasoning. Although aware that between his own desires and the evolution of the disease there is no relationship other than that established by appropriate actions, very often even the most rational and scientific person can use, at times, magical reasoning. Sometimes, to make them acceptable both to oneself and to others, magical actions are performed in a playful way ("it's just a game I don't really believe in"), or treated as a social custom ("I go to the healer because everyone goes there"). Other times it is the adherence itself to therapy, as well as the logical actions required by it, to be associated with a magical ritual; just think of the obsessional, completely ritual, treatment with which drugs are administered.

Occasional, isolated and playful forms of magical thinking should be accepted with disease, not forgetting that magism also permeates many evolved human expressions, such as art. Magic reasoning becomes a problem when it is strong and persistent, and leads to abandoning consolidated therapies to venture into senseless and often expensive practices, to which dependence on a charismatic figure is often not extraneous. To counteract the use of magism, it is necessary first of all to reflect on the function it performs, in order not to incur the easy shortcut of accusing the patient of pathological regression and credulity.

As has been said, a first function of magism is cognitive. The recourse to magical thinking and the abandonment of scientific therapeutic practices are all the greater when the patient has less of an understanding of the causes of their illness itself, its evolution and possible developments. Here we touch on a topic about which the situation of our health service is very critical. Although doctors who treat chronic patients in general are much more attentive than others to these aspects, there remains much to be done, while taking into account the objective difficulties of understanding and forecasting in chronic disease. It is necessary to dedicate time to explain to a patient, in understandable terms and taking into account their cultural level, with the help of concrete support systems, not only with words, the causes of one's illness, the reason for a therapy, the reasons for a certain decision. We need to be patient in listening to the patient and their questions, and even more in putting them in the condition of feeling authorized to ask and express their doubts, not feeling compelled to say "yes" even when nothing is understood. This work can be done in part individually and in part in groups, both to save time and to promote the diffusion of knowledge among patients and the discussion between them.

Greater knowledge about a disease and its evolution makes it less threatening; thus, the use of magism is reduced as a means to defend yourself and exorcise a danger that you cannot face in any other way. The use of magism as a defensive function is less not only when the patient's need for knowledge is addressed, but also when emotional needs are recognized and accepted. A sick person who can talk about his fears, without being ridiculed but treated seriously, needs less recourse to magical thinking. Even the use of magic as propitiation is reduced if specific requests are made to the person and if he/she is involved in actions in which he/she is the active force to focus on. In this sense, all the measures aimed at promoting self-efficacy through the action of the patient play a role in contrasting magical thought and action.

In short, it must be clear that it is not enough to execute the use of magism and consider it a regression to be condemned and contrasted by appealing to logical thinking. The use of magical thinking is reduced if people are put in a position to understand what is happening to them, if they are reassured, if they find doctors and a health facility to rely on with peace of mind, if they are asked to perform actions understanding their sense, with which they can exercise control.

With the exception of a very few, in the case of severe cognitive and cultural limits, everyone can understand simple and concrete explanations, in a context of attentive listening and participatory involvement. It is impressive how extremely efficient healthcare facilities are technologically, yet completely blind to the patient's fears and his anxiety to know and understand, this technical efficiency translates into failure, because in the end the patient will abandon these facilities. Putting the patient, with his intelligence and his emotions, at the center of the therapeutic intervention is the only way to counter the use of magical thinking. Do not delude yourself to achieve this goal only by reiterating the inconsistency and absurdity of the various magical practices, or by covering them with ridicule: the patient will continue to use them equally, with all the negative consequences on a therapeutic and economic level, if one does not find a willingness in doctors and healthcare personnel to address the continuous need to understand, to be reassured, to act.

Chapter 18

Telling the story of one's illness

Anyone who has visited waiting rooms of clinics or doctor's offices even without being a chronically ill patient, knows how common it is for people to talk about themselves, their situation and their illnesses. This need becomes even more evident in specialist centers, where people who share the same disease meet for tests and treatments. There is a profound need to talk about oneself which is almost completely ignored and misunderstood by health services and the people who work there. The lack of time, so often invoked, is not the only reason. In fact, the profound value of telling the story of one's illness, is not, as it may seem, an unnecessary waste of time. It is therefore worth reflecting on this aspect, because it concerns an important need of the psyche, not only for purposes of consolation. It is not only the need for a simple outlet and comfort that people speak to their interlocutors who may be interested at times but often also embarrassed, or reluctant.

Starting from Jerome Bruner's pioneering works, studies of narrative have taught us that storytelling is a way of knowing reality and giving order to the world and one's own history. If from a very young age a child is involved in adult narratives, from the moment one learns to speak we enter very simple stories, in which logical reasoning is inserted and takes on form. In our daily lives, first as a child and then as an adult, we build stories especially in the presence of "non-canonical" events, that is to say deviant from the ordinary and usual flow of events. The story is used to order, make understandable and communicable, and last but not least to better remember, these events that do not fall within known schemes; in this way even the most unusual, dramatic and unacceptable events find an explanation and acquire meaning.

It is therefore not surprising that people spontaneously resort to telling their story when faced with illness, which is, along with death, one of the events that most dramatically upset people's lives. The disease represents a serious caesura, because after the diagnosis everything will be different: now we know those strange and incomprehensible symptoms have a name, often fearful; that the future looks uncertain and unfavorable, which will present difficulties every day. The disease upsets all the concrete plans that a person had built for work, family and affections – distorting the optimistic trust we have in the future, as well as our world view and expectations toward life. For this reason, as we have seen, it is often experienced as an injustice, as an inexplicably wicked event that one has been struck with.

In this situation, storytelling is a powerful tool for finding coherence in ourselves and in what happens to us. Through the story we try to find an order, to give back a sense to our life devastated by illness, to redesign identity. The story allows the order to be reborn where the disease had wreaked havoc. This operation cannot take place only in the closed part of our mind, through the inner language, even if the dialogue with ourselves is important, since only we know our internal reactions, physical upheavals, sensations, images and thoughts that make up our emotional experience. Although the inner language is essential for rethinking one's own experience, for ordering emotions, for understanding what we are experiencing, it is not enough, however, because it lacks an external interlocutor: the point of view of others, by definition decentralized with respect to ours, it is essential to focus on aspects of which we are unable to realize. Only the social confrontation helps to overcome our self-centered perspective and allows us to see our situation from the outside. But others are helpful not only because they offer a different point of view, they allow us to build a socially shared story, attributing new meaning to our circumstances. The result is a combination of personal elaboration, and social validation. Our autobiography, from a personal event, thus becomes a social event.

For these reasons, one's story is an indispensable tool not only to find comfort, participation, help and advice, but in a more profound way, above all to redefine our identity, our projects and how to carry them out together with others. As we have seen, this redefinition of identity is particularly demanding in chronic disease, because it is necessary to face the continuous, mostly pejorative, changes it introduces.

Telling one's illness to a doctor, a nurse, but also to one's family and friends and even to strangers, becomes a way to find oneself and one's own potential for development. There is a need to give attention to this, particularly in healthcare facilities, the places where, among corridors, clinics and wards, a patient tries to find a response to their story, even from strangers they encounter casually. It is not difficult or costly to organize groups of patients dedicated to storytelling or to stimulate patients to express themselves either in oral or written narration, when possible. Where this is done, the results have been very good, because a patient has been helped to develop a positive image of themselves through their story, to rebuild a new identity, to sort out find sense in what is happening to them. In fact, there is a close relationship between the construction of personal stories and the development of a person.

To achieve these goals, in some cases self-help and mutual help groups may be sufficient, in which people mobilize their resources in helping others and in doing so simultaneously help themselves, gradually building a positive self-image. Self-help and mutual help groups are useful where the normal relational skills prevail, such as empathy; it must not be forgotten that helping others strongly favors individual well-being. On the other hand, these groups are not sufficient when the problems posed by the disease are such as to require the presence of a professional who favors the development of more adaptive and constructive ways of dealing with a disease in a short time. Also comparing oneself with people who are at a more advanced stage of a disease can be a source of anguish and pessimism. The advantage enjoyed by self-help and mutual aid groups in public health is certainly positive, but for various health services they cannot become a comfortable pretext for not investing money and professional resources where they are indispensable.

Part IV

There is a difference between "temperate" and "hardened." Often, this is not taken into consideration today. …

It seems to me, fearing our poor body is an exaggeration. The spirit is forgotten, left to curl up and wither away in some corner.

Chapter 19

The therapeutic relationship

More than thirty years have passed since Gigi Ghirotti told his story of adventure as a patient in Italian hospitals, breaking the taboo of silence on cancer, that "incurable disease" whose name could not even be stated. Despite the many grey areas, it must be recognized that much has changed for the better since then. In Ghirotti's writing, the journalist ironically recalled the proclamations aimed at making a patient the protagonist of their illness. Even if they were isolated voices, immediately denied within the concrete hospital reality, nevertheless those exhortations began to question established habits. It was no coincidence, then, that they came from diabetologists, that is, from doctors who cared for chronic patients. To cure the chronically ill it is imperative to involve them in the understanding and treatment of a disease that must be managed for years in their daily life; it is therefore precisely from the treatment of this type of disease that a different relationship between doctor and patient has slowly emerged, and more generally between patient and healthcare professional. The substantial reason is that chronic disease cannot be addressed without the active collaboration of the patient themselves, being the protagonist capable of effectively managing their disease in everyday life. It follows that the patient cannot passively delegate to the doctor the treatment of the disease and its recovery; for their part, the doctor and the nursing staff cannot neglect to involve the patient in the understanding of the disease and its treatment. The result is a continuous and rather close relationship in which the subjectivity of the patient cannot be ignored and excluded: a relationship today described by many as a relationship between partners who work together for the same purpose. Continuity is essential, even if the health organization does not always manage to guarantee it, because without it there is no collaborative therapeutic relationship.

From what I have personally experienced, the doctors and health personnel who deal with chronically ill people generally exhibit a relationship with their patients of a higher quality than that found on average in the health services. It must be acknowledged that dealing with chronically ill patients is very difficult and tiring on a psychological level: it is a matter of treating people who not only will never recover, but who do not improve except for short periods, and who on the contrary tend to get worse. It is not possible for healthcare professionals to have a fleeting relationship with the chronically ill, for example, as a surgeon does with their patients: on the contrary, a continuous relationship must be established over time, in which certain attitudes of distance, of disengagement or even worse of arrogance cannot continue. In this ongoing relationship, alongside some rewarding moments, the doctor and the health personnel know many other difficult and frustrating ones: when, despite all the efforts, the patient gets worse, refuses the therapy, does not accept the advice, does not collaborate, he pours his anxieties, his bad moods on the doctor, he demands an impossible miracle.

The bond that is created between doctor and patient over the years is important and strong, but precisely for this reason it is not free from conflicts, incomprehension and misunderstandings. I believe there is a self-selection in healthcare professionals: those who love to play the role of the savior, or rather that of the star, who love to pose as *deus ex machina*, or those who have cynical and detached attitudes, are unsuitable of caring for chronically ill patients, and if by mistake, they have embarked upon this work, they usually leave it. To care for the chronically ill, one must have: patience, tolerance to frustration, ability to put oneself in others' shoes, a will to establish meaningful and equal relationships with a patient and to build long-lasting and resistant therapeutic alliances.

The relationship between doctor and patient cannot be compared to that between a client and a professional, like an architect or a lawyer. The work of the doctor carries a particular weight, since their interventions concern the body and health of people, and often the alternative between life and death, or in any case between suffering and well-being. For this reason, it is possible to attribute to a doctor miraculous powers, meaning unrealistic expectations can be placed upon them, which can be completely unfounded and unreal, consequently making them the target of very strong resentments. The healthcare system itself has made the relationship even more complex, because the relationship is no longer governed by a direct exchange of money, even if the payment of the service in itself has never guaranteed reciprocity, nor has it ever placed the two roles on a level of equality, precisely because of the power exercised by the doctor over body and life.

In most cases, like Italy, the service is offered by the doctor on the basis of a commitment that he or she has made with a national health service, which the patient helps to finance through taxes. The relationship of reciprocity is thus more indirect and sometimes impersonal, but also more free and open with greater possibilities but also with some weak points. Let us recall that for some patients, the sense of control in a relationship governed by bargaining and money may be lacking, prompting negative claims and uncooperative attitudes. It is therefore necessary to recover a different reciprocity, founded on the one hand on the common humanity of the actors in the relationship, recognized as people worthy of respect, and on the other in cooperation for the same shared purpose, which is the well-being of sick. In this partnership- relationship, the doctor and healthcare personnel make available their competence and professionalism by virtue of a commitment made with society, while a patient gives their willingness to collaborate. Only this cooperation, which fortunately takes place more often than is believed, allows the treatment and personal development of the patient in the best conditions allowed by the disease.

In this regard, it should be remembered that the same communication between a doctor and a patient, apparently so obvious and trivial, is already an act of cooperation. In fact, communication is never a one-way transmission of knowledge and information; it is the common construction of shared meanings, which engages both actors – the listener and the speaker – in mutual attention and understanding. For this reason, good communication is never separated from empathy and the ability to put yourself in the other's shoes, it is a negotiation in which cognitive aspects are intertwined with the emotional and motivational ones. So, it is not only what is said that counts, but the way in which it is said, both verbally and non-verbally, as well as the conditions under which communication takes place. Certain conversations at the door of a clinic, or being continuously disturbed by cell phone rings or other types of interruptions, cannot give rise to good communication, even if the content is formally correct and truthful. Also, certain attitudes of detachment nearing annoyance toward the chronically ill, as if their requests were absurd claims, considering one's incurable condition, frustrate and limit the value of any correct medical prescription.

Chapter 20

Trust

In order to cooperate, the chronically ill, even more than any other patient, must establish a relationship of trust with the doctors and the staff of the facility that is taking care of them: however, this trust is never given once for all, it is built with patience over time. But what does trust in a doctor consist of? Certainly not in delegating to them the solution of all problems, much less in considering them as an omnipotent magician or an infallible thaumaturge. Trust is turning to a doctor with the conviction that they, according to their knowledge and sense of responsibility, according to science and conscience, can act in the best possible way for the benefit of a patient, collaborating with them assuming the role of responsibility.

The feeling of trust has its roots in early childhood experiences with the figure of mother, with the so-called attachment figures, and grows and sharpens over the course of development, becoming more selective. Trust is the basis of many behaviors in our daily social life, and for this reason economists are also interested in it today, who consider it one of the foundations for trade and economic exchange. In our social life trust is indispensable, in fact it is much more widespread than we commonly think. For example, it is based on trust that we board a plane entrusting our lives to pilots and technicians that we do not know, that we will never see and that we know nothing about: paying a ticket and respecting some rules of behavior, we expect to have a reliable and safe service in return, provided according to shared and respected rules.

Igniting trust in social relations between adults requires reciprocity and a sense of responsibility on both sides. In the therapeutic relationship, the practice of informed consent represents, at least theoretically, the formal recognition of the responsibility of both actors in the relationship: the patient on the one hand and the doctor and the healthcare structure on the other. Unfortunately, it is often reduced to a purely bureaucratic procedure where the patient signs a consent form that in actuality they do not understand. Yet it is a potentially important moment to strengthen the trust relationship, if accompanied by time, explanation, dialogue, information, comparison, and effort in distinguishing scientific knowledge from opinions and personal beliefs.

Trust is undermined by all situations where reciprocity and a sense of responsibility are lacking. Often, some doctors and health services pay the price of negative behavior of other professionals: in fact, patient are reduced to generalize, in moments of despair and anger, episodes of incompetence, disorganization, including lack of honesty. Certainly a patient cannot have confidence in a doctor if they have doubts about their competence, if they find an organizational context that nullifies their excellent professional skills, if a patient is perplexed by the doubt that a certain therapy was offered to them not because at that moment it was what was best for them, but because the doctor receives greater economic compensation, or in any case a material advantage that is foreign and perhaps contrary to the patient's well-being. In general, the economic and moral aspects of unprofessional, ineffective or dishonest behavior are highlighted, forgetting the negative consequences they have on the patient's ability to cope with the disease. In fact, the doubt of not being treated correctly, of not receiving adequate care, of not seeing one's patient rights respected, translates into a greater sense of vulnerability and helplessness. Fears about the morality of healthcare management in general, and about a doctor's behavior specifically, solicits one's sense of impotency in living with disease; on the contrary, a patient's strength of mind rests on the critically important point of trusting that they being treated fairly, of not being a victim of favoritism, but of being seriously considered and properly cared for.

The professionalism and morality of a healthcare facility and its staff are a primary factor in offering strength that enhances positive attitudes in a patient; on the contrary, health injustice is a factor of psychological vulnerability, as well as a cause of objective damage. Even when – and they are the most frequent cases – it is not a question of dishonesty, but of disorganization and inability to effectively coordinate the different components of the healthcare structure, the effect is the same and the subjective vulnerability is increased.

It should not be hidden that the reality of chronic disease, as a pathology for which there are no resolutive therapies, in particular the treatment of some symptoms can be very difficult, this can put to test a patient trust in a doctor and in the healthcare structure itself. It is more than normal for a patient, exasperated by the lack of results, to ask oneself – are these therapies right for me? Are they really the most suitable given what is available for my disease today? Perhaps the doctor is too cautious about new drugs or, on the contrary, too adventurous? Are there any pharmaceuticals available on the US or European market not yet approved in my country due to sheer bureaucratic delay? Why has nobody ever told me about trial experiments that are taking place? Must I continue to be treated by that center? What if I were to go abroad?

These and many other questions crowd the chronically ill mind, which often does not dare to propose them to a doctor. In recent years, the widespread Internet access has widened the possibility for everyone to have information on therapies, with the result of being often overwhelmed by an avalanche of news and data, many of which are venal and unfounded. Not having knowledge and reference frameworks that allow you not to lose the compass in this navigation, the patient risks being lost or falling victim to bogus, ineffective, illusory and expensive therapeutic proposals (see Part VI). In this way, one's bewilderment can grow, prompting doubt toward the therapies and treatments one is following, and sometimes even their diagnosis, not only in the early phase but also after many years. We should not be surprised by these hesitations and these anxieties: their recurrence is normal in an illness that lasts for a lifetime, without solutions only progressive worsening.

More than ever in times of difficulty only a frank and solid relationship trusting a doctor allows the patient not to get lost and to make inappropriate choices. The relationship of trust is essential for adherence to therapy, in a relationship of collaboration and not of imposition, in which the patient's resistance and refusal must also be recognized and accepted. Especially in the most critical moments, when faced with a proposal for very invasive, devastating and uncertain therapeutic interventions, the ability of the doctor and the healthcare facility to gain the patient's confidence but also to respect their decision is measured. The recourse to the judicial authority to impose the therapy, which unfortunately is sometimes seen, is the dramatic sign of the failure to try to establish a meaningful relationship with the patient.

Chapter 21

Empathy

Empathy (from the German term *Einfühlung*, "to feel inside") is the ability to share the emotions of others without confusing either oneself with others or one's own emotions with theirs. It is an experience of consonant and appropriate emotional participation that is frequent in all meaningful human relationships, first of all friendship and love. Even if it is an emotional experience, cognitive components are relevant in it, specifically the ability to recognize and distinguish correctly and differentiating the emotions expressed by another person, both through body and word; representing one's state of being, and experiences, as different from their own.

For these characteristics, empathy is different from emotional contagion, in which the absence of a differentiation between self and other causes an automatic and involuntary affective sharing, which translates into an immediate motor imitation (for example, without realizing it, assuming the posture and the expression of another). Contagion does not imply discrimination of the emotional states of others, nor does it mean the vicarious nature of one's sharing is understood. It has its neurophysiological foundation in the "mirror neurons," which are the basis of the automatic imitative behaviors: they are activated when one animal observes another making a movement, also present in the human species. Contagion is not limited to childhood, where it has an important and useful role in the mother-child relationship, but can also appear in adulthood, for example in the relationship between lovers or in a crowd. It should be emphasized that for an adult person who is aware of his individuality, contagion, outside of a personal emotional relationship, is experienced as a danger.

The simpler forms of empathy, which even young children are capable of, do not disappear in adulthood, but are still characterized by self-centeredness: in fact, we tend to attribute to others the emotions that we ourselves generally experience in a similar situation. This allows the understanding and sharing of the emotions of others, but not yet the full representation of their experience, with the result that the help actions that follow are not decentralized: thus a child who sees a sad adult consoles them by offering their own teddy bear, as the adult comforts her/his friend with words that would help themselves in a similar situation. The most advanced forms of empathy are instead mediated by the ability to understand that the experiences of others can be different from one's own and to participate in it equally; for example, we can participate in the emotion of sadness experienced by a sick person, even if in a similar situation we would rather react with anger. Only this second type of empathy allows real help to others, not by doing what might be of relief to us at that moment, but by acting consonantly with the needs of the other, well differentiated and distinct from our own. This form or evolved empathy is an essential skill in a context, such as health care, which often imposes its routines of superficiality and inattention, without knowing how to put itself in the shoes of others (as in the increasingly frequent case of a radio turned on at full volume in a clinic), imposing its own choices and vision of the world, without taking into consideration the point of view of its patients.

In the relationship of care, it is essential that there is the capacity for empathetic sharing, without which, a patient will be treated as an inert body void of emotions and interiority, rather than as a person. On the contrary, contagion is to be avoided, both because it does not allow any help for a patient and because it exposes the health worker to an unsustainable and destructive emotional form of participation, particularly dangerous when the relationship is continuous, as in the case of a chronically ill patient. Even if it is not always clear, health workers are aware of the dangers of contagion, revealing concern toward its dismantling power. Unfortunately, the ability to share in a mature way without the influence of contagion is often missing.

In the absence of professional tools that allow healthcare professionals to avoid contagion but permit empathetic sharing, they often use denial and blindness as a preventive defense. Like when you avoid talking and deepening the experiences of the patient, or avoid looking them in the face in order not to unwillingly grasp their negative expressions, or as when you take refuge in technicality and action, or, conversely, in theatrical attitudes of concern that pretend exaggerated attention. In some severe cases, the objectification of a patient is reached, in which numerous examples can be given: referring to a patient by a term that designates their pathology or with the number of their hospital bed instead of one's name; chatting with colleagues while performing disturbing and painful health practices on a patient's body, as if they were repairing an object; speaking in a futile, incessant and exaggerated way, well beyond a normal attempt to distract attention, preventing any dialogue. Since one can be of no help without participation, denying a patient's suffering can sometimes permit technically correct practices, but not an effective, long-lasting therapeutic relationship.

The belief that healthcare professionals cannot be of any help to patients when they themselves are victims of contagion (inhibiting their ability to perform the necessary medical practices because they are overwhelmed by emotion) is entirely founded. But what some do not understand is that it is possible to participate in the suffering of others by avoiding such emotional contagion, indeed guaranteeing support and help. In short, the danger of emotional contagion cannot justify the lack of empathy. The ability to know how to share in a professional and differentiated way, with a distance that allows one to participate in the suffering of others without feeling overrun, must be included throughout the education, training and professional path of all health workers. And this is particularly necessary for those who work with chronically ill patients. Facing a patient who presents the same symptoms, and indeed ones that become more aggravating over time, requires knowing how to modulate empathetic sharing in a professional mature way, so as not to become overwhelmed by it.

Chapter 22

The patient between statistical logic and clinical logic

It is not uncommon for a patient to complain of feeling treated as a number and not as a person with a specific physical and psychological individuality. This widespread sentiment refers to one of the most critical aspects in the relationship between the doctor and a patient in a therapy setting: the use of statistical rather than clinical logic. To understand the terms of this problem it is appropriate to spotlight these two forms of reasoning, which serve different purposes.

Logical-paradigmatic thinking has been defined as "extensional," since it seeks universally valid general laws (for example, how the heart works in humans), builds classifications (adults and the elderly), establishes causal links (a specific bacterium as the cause of a disease), studies the individual case in relation to more general categories (the disease that occurs in the patient as a specific case of a disease). This type of thinking privileges probabilistic reasoning and statistics (how much, for example, exposure to smoking increases the probability of getting cancer). In this type of thought, the individual case is of interest not in itself, but in that it is related to general categories, according to a vertical process of subordination and superordination. The wealth and variability of individual situations is therefore sacrificed to extensionality and the search for general laws that go beyond the individual case.

Clinical thinking, on the other hand, is typically "intensional" and applies to the individual case, considered and studied in depth in its irreducible specificity. In trying to understand a single situation, this type of thinking does not sacrifice richness and variability but tries to preserve them and analyze them to recompose a unitary picture. No general laws are sought, applicable according to rules and constants; the attention is centered on the specific case, of which we try to understand the antecedents, the characteristics and the potential evolution. Intensional thought forms are not at a lower level than extensional forms, but accompany them, responding to a logic other than paradigmatic, functional for different purposes.

Intensional thinking uses particular reasoning strategies, such as the heuristic of representativeness, which considers some events as better representative of a given category. The use of this heuristic process in paradigmatic thinking and probabilistic reasoning is in error, because the events that best represent a specific category are considered as more probable. In reality the opposite is true, since an event is all the more improbable when its distinctive features are numerous. For example, a man over 55 years old, a smoker and a heavy eater, with a family history of cardiac arrests, is a primary representative of the category with a greater risk of heart attack; people with all these characteristics, however, are less numerous on a statistical level, compared to the overall population, and it is therefore more unlikely to meet an individual with all these traits. On the contrary, the use of the representativeness heuristic is indispensable on a clinical level, because it allows the doctor to pay attention to those groups and individuals who are most at risk for their health.

Paradigmatic and clinical thinking must coexist if we want to respond to the immense problems of knowledge and treatment that chronic disease poses, and if we want to avoid the frequent errors of reasoning that can lead to erroneous decisions. Paradigmatic thinking, precisely in so far as it is not interested in the case itself, if not as an aspect of a more general category, it is not possible to constitute the only or principal method of reasoning when the treatment of a patient is undertaken. It is on the basis of paradigmatic thinking and a statistical evaluation that the usefulness of a therapy is subjected to verification through the analysis of large studies and judged positive or not. But it is on the basis of clinical logic that the doctor evaluates the advisability of a specific therapy, at a certain moment, facing a specific patient: it is the patient, and not the disease, who must be treated. Every chronically ill patient knows how difficult this assessment can be and how many defeats a doctor and patient can face. Therapies that have shown a high probability of being effective can prove completely useless for a certain person, and others identified as low risk can be very harmful for a specific patient.

In healthcare practice today there are two opposing situations that are equally inequitable and risky. On one hand, the patient is mechanically applied therapeutic protocols that have shown validity in experiments with large numbers, without bothering to adapt them to an individual patient given their biological, psychological and relational specificities. In these cases, there is a lack of clinical thinking and the patient is not considered as a specific case to be understood and treated, but simply as a particular case of a general class. This is precisely what patients perceive when they complain that they are treated as numbers and not as people, as diseases and not as ill, and when they denounce their specificities as being ignored. In the worst cases it even seems a patient is not a person to be treated, but rather a case to be included in a trial, national or international, of which they know nothing or very little about.

On the contrary, the patient may be faced with therapeutic proposals which present themselves as attentive to their biological and psychological specificity, as well as to the overall relationship between these aspects, but which are not based on sufficient validation. Clinical ability, instead, consists in knowing how to use the tools and knowledge that derive from paradigmatic thinking, and therefore also from the results of trial experiments, within a practice that takes into account the specificity of the individual case, irreducible to any general law or significantly influenced by the context. The proposal of therapies that seem to be highly individualized, but where one cannot see a solid scientific foundation, is a concrete risk and a source of tension for the patient. I recall my anxiety when a doctor proposed to use a set of chemical substances and various drugs (not specific to my pathology) with unproven methods and dosages. It was a proposal that seemed tempting, since the usual therapies had not worked. But I refused, because I trusted the specialist who treated me and I did not consider this doctor's therapeutic intervention sufficiently founded: I did not want to be a guinea pig and I was afraid of procuring more damage than good. The physician's highly critical attitude toward internationally recognized therapies, the accusation of passivity toward me, the threat of the terrible consequences that I was facing, weighed heavily on my decision. I feared to put my health and my life in the hands of an exalted person, who resorted to any psychological manipulation to convince patients and who sought a significant economic return. But in any case, it was a difficult choice, and some doubt remains that I have never been able to completely silence, feeling that perhaps I have missed a potentially useful opportunity.

It must be recognized that difficulties in the treatment of chronic disease very often lead the doctor and the patient to move to a shaded area, where choices are difficult and the points of reference are uncertain. Since in many cases commonly used drugs are ineffective or have too many negative side effects, people go in search of new therapies, even unusual and less secure ones, and also of new drugs, perhaps promising but not yet sufficiently tested. Often doctors may find themselves perplexed, not wanting to ignore therapeutic proposals that could be useful on one hand, and on the other not wanting to take the risk with dangerous interventions yet to be proven effective. On the part of the patient they may show resistance toward experimental therapies, those that are still in trial or even with new therapies, as a patient may feel lost or betrayed when a consolidated therapy is dismissed or overcome by new discoveries. In all these cases, only a solid relationship of trust and a frank communication between a patient and doctor allow decisions to be faced without risks, in an evaluation of the costs and benefits while taking into account the whole person.

The clinical attitude toward the patient is in fact based on attention to the totality of his person, understood as a system in which body and psyche are in continuous interaction and in which the different parts of the body are in close connection with each other. This holistic view of the person, and of the body itself, is today strongly lacking in health practice, above all outside the services that constantly provide for the chronically ill. In the current health and hospital organization, both when it accompanies the diagnosis and afterwards, a patient often has the impression that not only is the relationship between mind and body ignored, but that the body itself is reduced to a sum of poorly assembled elements, of which every specialist sees only a piece without having a vision of totality. In this way, not only is the patient not taken into consideration, but neither is the disease.

This fragmentation of interventions is a cause of serious errors and wasted time, as well as a source of tremendous tension and disorientation for a patient; yet it does not seem that much attention has been paid to overcoming this by healthcare facilities, remaining engulfed in habits that seem to be unchangeable. The issue is both cultural and organizational, looking at the relationships between various specialists and the one doctor who is treating a patient for their specific pathology, together with the not to be forgotten so-called primary care physician. These two figures in particular are important points of reference for the patient because they are stable and continuous; but exchanges between them are currently insufficient to say the least and mostly mediated by the patient herself. The latter will often be in the uncomfortable position of having to recompose a unifying framework, without having the skills or emotional detachment, and most of all being in the middle of a worrisome and destructive dynamic.

Chapter 23

Alternative medicine

If it is necessary to admit with humility that the knowledge of human beings, of our diseases and of their treatment does not belong only to Western medicine, it must however also be recognized, this time with pride, that the latter has achieved in diverse sectors extraordinary and inalienable results. Western medicine owes its successes to a scientific approach in which the body is studied as an objective reality to be investigated with objective methods, coherently with other sciences (such as physics and chemistry), while therapeutic attempts are subjected to experimental verification and validated through falsification. It is scientific medicine that is referred to when it comes to official medicine, recognized by health services throughout Western countries.

In recent years, Western medicine has been contrasted with other medicines, referred to as "alternative." Under this term, a heterogeneous number of therapies, very different in their cultural origin, theoretical bases, substances used, tests carried out, are united: treatments with herbs, medicine from non-Western cultures, homeopathy, para-psychological interventions, iridology and much more, up to practices of clear magical imprint.

Interestingly, phytotherapy is the closest to official medicine, since chemical compounds are not synthesized in a laboratory but through the use of plants, of which the effectiveness is based on empirical knowledge and sometimes also on experimentation. For centuries, in fact, medicine has used herbs as the main pharmacological remedy and also today a number of drugs are derived directly from plants or contain substances originally discovered in the plant world and subsequently produced in the laboratory. This type of therapy is therefore not necessarily an alternative to official medicine, provided the efficacy of the numerous substances of plant origin is validated. In the medicines of other cultures, above all Chinese medicine, the therapeutic intervention is placed within a conception of the world and of the person, which is very far from Western thought; however, this does not mean that all suggested practices are groundless. For example, acupuncture, characteristic of Chinese medicine, is increasingly validated and has found confirmation also at the scientific level – the WHO has compiled a list of pathologies that can be treated with this therapy. The case of homeopathy is perhaps the most debated, since it presents itself as a complementary modality to official medicine, by proposing to treat diseases not with antagonistic substances but on the contrary with similar substances. The representatives of medical science contest the generalization of this principle and argue that, with the dilutions carried out, homeopathic remedies on a chemical level no longer contain any active principle beyond the therapeutic power of a glass of fresh water.

But, in essence, what distinguishes alternative medicines from official Western medicine? The discriminant lies in the systematic and objective verification of the usefulness of a therapy. Experimentation in medicine aims to distinguish personal and subjective beliefs about the efficacy of a therapy from the objective demonstrations of its effective value. All scientific research tries to overcome self-deception, stereotypes, entrenched beliefs, erroneous evaluations, through the systematic use of methodologies and tools that guarantee the objectivity of the findings as much as possible. Psychology can only agree with this approach. In fact, since its beginnings, with studies on optical illusions, it has shown that many of our perceptions and knowledge are deceptive and distorted. Just think of the heuristics of availability, where events, mentally recalled with greater ease, due to their strong emotional relevance, are wrongly considered as more probable. The use of these heuristics is frequent in daily life, being useful for the speed of the evaluations they allow, but it is fallacious in paradigmatic thinking, when for example they are used as a demonstration of the effectiveness of a therapy. Similarly, the tendency to establish cause-effect relationships on the basis of simple temporal contiguity (*post hoc, ergo propter hoc:* after this, therefore because of this), a shortcut so frequent in daily action, has no logical foundation. Still, many believe that to prove the validity of a hypothesis it is enough to find many cases that confirm it, when, on the contrary, it is necessary to demonstrate that there are no cases that falsify it.

In order not to fall into these traps and shortcuts, scientific research relies on logical-paradigmatic thinking, which uses the experimental method as an instrument of choice and makes use of statistics and a probability assessment. Therapies that have shown, in respect to a control group, to be more effective than "chance" are considered valid. In fact, it is known that there may be improvements and even healing completely independent of specific therapies. Just think of the well-known "placebo effect" (of which the neurophysiological foundations are now being discovered), which clearly highlights the very close link between the psyche and body: the intake of a substance without therapeutic effects has the power to improve the patient's condition, when one is convinced of its effectiveness.

The conditions of chronic disease make a patient particularly vulnerable to the appeal of alternative medicines, specifically due to one having an incurable disease, a reality so difficult to accept. If official medicine, despite all its impressive scientific and techno-logical apparatuses, is unable to heal or alleviate serious symptoms, the patient finds it legitimate and almost necessary to turn to other medicines, even when one is not intimately convinced of their effect-iveness. In fact, one believes they are not risking anything, and that an opportunity may be missed by not trying them. Here, alongside the natural curiosity of the human being, is when the desire to act personally comes into play, rebelling against the inaction into which the lack of effective cures forces many patients, who, after having tried all the official therapies, find that they recognize no therapy is useful to them, let alone a solution. Then the desire to try alter-native medicines may arise, both to demonstrate to oneself and to others that they leave no stone unturned, in the genuine hope of finding an answer where official medicine has failed.

Turning to the use of alternative medicines seems to be a claim to one's subjectivity. Through individual choice, outside the official circuit of health services, and therefore with its own direct eco-nomic involvement, people affirm not only their ability to act, but exercising their ability to choose and make decisions. A transgres-sive attitude toward medicine dispensed from health services, often increased by mistrust toward the doctor and more generally of the public service, may not be foreign. The same economic commitment can be seen by some as a way to manage the therapeutic relation-ship firsthand in a condition of equality and not of subordination. In a more radical way, the affirmation of subjectivity passes through the refusal of the specialist competence of a doctor and official medicine in general, to claim one's decision-making power, one's choices, one's subjective ability to evaluate and judge what can be useful and what not.

In the Western world, the widespread diffusion of alternative therapies, which is greater among people of middle education, seems in short to be attributable to the widespread attempt to recover their own subjectivity, to the refusal of approval in the official medicine dispensed to everyone. In reality, paradoxically, the affirmation of one's individuality passes, in this as in many other cases, precisely through adherence to fashion and therefore through a new form of approval. No wonder this tendency is particularly felt in the disease, which deeply questions one's subjectivity and one's life. This recovery of subjectivity is however often illusory, since many of these therapeutic proposals require uncritical adherence, if not total delegation and subordination to a healer or a holy person.

The shortcoming of scientific culture, including the refusal of science and technology, are serious and widespread in many countries; they are also sometimes combined with disillusionment, meaning what follows unfulfilled promises. For the former, the main culprits are education and mass media, while official medicine has also contributed to disillusionment – as its often triumphalistic tones have done nothing but cultivate disbelief. At the same time, touting contempt toward all knowledge derived from other cultures and disciplines. This arrogance of official medicine produced a boomerang effect, prompting individual interest in alternative medicine. But what is even more conducive to disaffection from scientific medicine is the lack of attention to the subjectivity of the patient, which manifests itself in many ways: the inability to take into consideration the totality of the person, as a being not only physical but also psychological; the disconnected interventions that fragment the body into many disconnected parts; communication and relationship errors; the lack of involvement of the patient in understanding the disease, in making therapeutic choices and their implementation, up to the forced imposition of the therapies. It is above all this inattention to the subjectivity of the patient that the use of alternative therapies can be traced, too hastily labeled as the fruit of ignorance and as magical reasoning. Although it is undeniable that many alternative therapies are accompanied by an apparatus of rites and symbols that favors magical reasoning, the latter alone is unable to explain its diffusion.

Once again, therefore, it is to a relationship of mutual collaboration between the patient, the doctor and the healthcare facility that we must appeal to correctly set up a treatment that refers to the parameters of scientific medicine. The sick person is able to resort to scientific medicine in a critical and conscious way, if they are helped to understand the disease at every moment of its evolution, if they are involved in therapeutic decisions and placed in the conditions to manage their disease in everyday life, if they can recover a sense of personal self-efficacy, and if their subjectivity and entirety as a person is acknowledged and respected. This is how in moments of doubt and failure, so frequent in the long course of the chronic disease, it will always be the patient's trust in the doctor and in the health structure that will divert him from potentially dangerous therapeutic adventures both physically and psychologically.

Chapter 24

Confidentiality

The right of respect for a patient's private sphere is one of the most overlooked and undervalued by our healthcare system; by the bureaucracy, by health workers and by the ill themselves. One has the impression that, in this as in other cases, habit and haste prevent doctors and nurses from realizing obvious violations instead from the outside. What about, for example, the folders, with the patient's data clearly highlighted, left on the office desk while other samples are being taken, and on which all those who pass by could glance? In these cases, a well-known phenomenon of habit comes into play, which leads to blindness and indifference toward aspects considered obvious and irrelevant. In this way, healthcare personnel no longer pay any attention to actions that have by now become habitual and routine, which, on the contrary, for the patient, are an essential part of his life and suffering. An experience I had while teaching in a professional nursing school, was that frequently first-year students pointed out and criticized aspects that the staff no longer noticed, which the students of the following years already tended to ignore. Meaning that the first-year students were scandalized by the brusque and rude ways in which blood samples were sometimes taken, while these methods left those who had worked in the clinics for years indifferent. Among the neglected aspects in wards and clinics there is, for example, leaving the door open on the corridor, without any respect for the patient's privacy. Thus, it happens that the patient undergoes blood sampling or a visit in front of all those who happen to be passing by that moment in the corridor. If the practice of keeping the door open is slightly less frequent in clinics, it is normal practice in hospital wards. From experience I know how much bewilderment the request to close the door arouses in nurses: sometimes they respond with a clear refusal and visible anxiety. In reality there is no valid excuse for this intrusion into the life of the patient, who often also constitutes a significant disturbance to his peace. It derives only from the habit and illusion of the health personnel to keep the situation under control by glancing, when passing through the corridor, to the hospital rooms. In reality there are quite different systems for monitoring the condition of the patient that a modern ward should have: today a hospital should no longer resemble a phalanstery.

Even the frenzy of hospital work can sometimes intervene in this decision. In this case, I remember an episode in which, lying on a bed near the entrance to the ward room, and tired of undergoing the gaze of all those who passed in the corridor as well as the disturbing noises that came from it, I asked to close the door. I was asked to put a screen next to the bed; to my objection that it was much easier to close the door, the nurse replied that it took longer to open the door. This answer clarifies the difficulties, although it cannot justify a practice that is a source of suffering and tension for the patient.

The worst violations of confidentiality, however, come from bureaucratic and medical offices. For example, a patient may have to shout through protective glass to make an appointment, or there may be a microphone that amplifies to all the room the kind of exam the patient is booking or the type of pathology to be indicated. If this is not painless in large cities, it can be disastrous in small towns, where everyone knows each other, creating not only embarrassment for the patient, but potentially for anyone using healthcare services. I remember, for example, the emotional upset of a very young girl when seeking a pregnancy test was revealed to all those who were waiting to book various exams, as well as the shame of a patient whose "exemption for pathology" had also been made known to all the bystanders waiting in line. I also recall the two makeshift desks placed a few centimeters from one other in a corridor for the renewal of the official declaration of exemption, where with evident embarrassment many people, myself included, after a long line elbow to elbow declared their pathology in a way that was easily audible by anyone.

In fact, not only with regard to confidentiality (here is a brief digression) most of the current bureaucracy of the health service is full of rules and procedures, often adverse to the patient. These rules are not justified, as we sometimes want to believe, by the need to save money or to avoid abuses. They derive solely from the inability of bureaucrats to see from the point of view of the ill and to imagine procedures that are functional in achieving the objective of treating patients in the best way possible. Their self-centered focus, combined with a hearty dose of rigidity, leads to procedures that are useful only to the offices that designed them, and not to health personnel, much less to the patients being treated. Hence the perspective is completely reversed and we lose sight of what should be the primary objective of any and all health services: guaranteeing the patient the best possible care and well-being. The examples are numerous and every patient could make a long list of them, varying according to different countries and health systems. I limit myself to mentioning two of my experiences: first, asking a specialist (whom I never met) to rewrite an order for a diagnostic examination already requested by the only regional specialist center; second, it was necessary (at that time of technology), to hand carry the specialist's order to my doctor and the reservation center to make an appointment, then return to the center in person to pick up the results and once again hand carry them to my doctor and to the specialist.

Returning to confidentiality, unfortunately it must be recognized that not even the ill and their relatives often show great attention. One episode in particular was in a hospital: at an internal reservation counter, the staff had mindfully placed a yellow line on the ground together with a very clear sign that asked people to remain behind the line when someone was at the counter. When I got there, I stopped before the line and waited for the person in front of me to finish their requests at the counter. I was immediately attacked by the people behind me, who demanded that I move forward, that is, directly behind the innocent person who was speaking at the counter, perhaps in the childish illusion that in this way the line would be shorter.

Even in the wards or rooms of day hospitals, unfortunately the attitude of relatives and friends is often too intrusive toward other hospitalized people. This intrusion is certainly not made with malicious intentions and is most often generated by anxiety and the need to reassure oneself through confrontation with those who are experiencing similar situations. Nonetheless, it is often a source of tension and discomfort for those who endure this. In particular, in our hospitals, where the rooms in most cases have no fewer than three beds, the ill are often restricted into forced cohabitation. Although economic, organizational and architectural justifications can be found for this condition, it increases a patient's malaise because it forces them to share intimacy with others and their relatives, precisely in moments of maximum suffering, when none of us do this willingly even when we are feeling well. There is much work to be done in this direction, together with all the people involved with disease and their different roles.

Part V

To free someone you love, completely freeing them to live their life, is the most difficult thing one can do.

People are reluctant to recognize that at a certain point one can do no more, but only accept and be.

Chapter 25

Us and the others

The human being has been rightly defined as biologically social, since our life and development are not possible outside the relationship with our own kind. The offspring of humans, who among all species have the longest childhood, if there is no one to take care of us for a significant number of years, we face death; moreover, we do not develop adequately unless there is someone who maintains a loving relationship with us, which is defined as an "attachment" figure. Our complete psychic development, even when it is strongly linked to genetic influences and neurophysiological development, as in the case of intelligence, is always mediated by social relations: as demonstrated in the cases of "wolf children," raised by animals, a child does not learn to speak, while being genetically predisposed to do so – speaking can happen only if there is a relationship with a human being who communicates with us.

Not only during the developmental age, but throughout life there is no personal realization outside of social relationships: even the most intimate thoughts are mediated by a social tool, such as language. The human being is biologically endowed with great expressive and communicative skills, and is designed to develop sophisticated social skills allowing us to establish long-lasting relationships with our own kind. Contrary to what is often believed in the name of a trivialized Darwinism, during the phylogenetic development the "survival of the fittest," understood as being the most aggressive, was not established, but the winner is the one who best knows how to live in a group, who is most able to recognize and share the emotions of others, establish collaborative relationships, protect and help companions.

Recognizing the profound sociability of the individual does not mean forgetting that each person wants to express his or her unique physical and psychological individuality. For this reason, each of us tends to realize ourselves by differentiating oneself from the others, opposing their attempts at overpowering, seducing or just even in similarity. This process takes place in relation to the attachment figures of our childhood, beginning with our parents, leading to adolescence which is a crucial and decisive time for affirmation – sometimes it is a clamorous and conflictual process to establish one's own differentiated and separate identity. This highlights the twofold need, which accompanies us throughout our lives, to establish meaningful and profound relationships, but at the same time to be oneself, to make our own choices autonomously, not to suffer constraints. Since the two needs may be in conflict, tensions are not uncommon, evident in many relationships of love and friendship: precisely where the bond is strongest, the fear of losing oneself in the other can be greater.

It is in the complexity of the relationships between "I" and "you" that we must reference to understand the particular situation in which the chronically ill person finds oneself in their relations with others, above all one's family. A patient needs others and their help, often to such an extent that one is unable to live alone, both temporarily (in the case of worsening) and permanently (in the case of disability). This condition of need can trigger a state of dependence on others, with various consequences. It may happen that a patient gives in to their dependency from which psychological advantages can derive both for oneself (feeling loved and cared for, even if at the cost of losing autonomy) and for their family (feeling useful, important or even superior). In this case, the risk is that the patient renounces personal development and actions that could still be allowed by the disease (such as going out alone) reacting to their self-denial with recurrent episodes of anger. On the contrary, a patient may claim an unrealistic autonomy, and pretend to do actions alone that could be dangerous for them. At the same time, the offer of normal help may be interpreted by a patient in a negative way, as an attempt to limit their autonomy, and responding aggressively. It is not uncommon for the sick to unload anger upon those who help them due to their loss of the ability to act alone, a feeling that they are unable to express differently and above all to overcome and resolve.

For these reasons it is essential that both a patient and their friends and family engage in clear effective communication, without distortions or manipulations. "Double-link communications" are defined as those contradictory messages that place those who receive them in the unpleasant situation of not knowing what to give importance to, and making mistakes regardless. For example, a phrase such as: "Go ahead, I am always alone", on one hand authorizes a family member to go out, while on the other it makes them feel guilty if one decides to go. Excess of verbal intervention should also be avoided, remembering that for a patient it is above all to be heard and their suffering accepted. One's expressions of pain does not immediately require advice, exhortations, or worse negations, however motivated by the desire to be positive. Often others are embarrassed facing a patient's psychological pain and are eager to say something proactive at all costs, ending up denying their suffering with phrases such as (the most common is that of many American TV series): "You will see, everything will go well", inappropriate suggestions, unsolicited incitements and ostentatious optimism. I recall the sense of estrangement and distance felt toward a friend who minimized my moment of serious deterioration: although motivated by the best intentions to highlight the positive aspects of the situation, those statements marked a profound incomprehension between us. In fact, many times a simple affirmation of participation (such as "I'm sorry") is worth more than many words that only serve to cover the speaker's anxiety and risk sending contradictory messages. Silence can also be useful, when it is meaningful between people who are willing and able to communicate on a non-verbal level, offering a closeness and understanding that words could not express better.

The ability to communicate effectively is particularly important in situations where help is needed; this is why today there is an insistence on self-efficacy, in asking for help as one of the basic skills which a patient must learn. As we have seen, self-efficacy concerns specific abilities, and knowing how to ask for help is indispensable for the well-being of a patient and for those who care for them. Again, the risks relate to two opposing attitudes: underestimating one's abilities and asking for help even when it is not needed, exposing oneself to addiction or refusal (both of family members and health workers), or, on the contrary, overestimating their own possibilities and not asking for help even when it could be indispensable, due to a misunderstood sense of autonomy and pride. Self-efficacy requires a lucid analysis of one's own potential, to be done in concert with oneself, a doctor, health personnel, friends and family members. In this way, it is possible to identify which actions are necessary and who to turn to in different situations of need, in order to be able to ask for help effectively. This evaluation must be continually updated, in relation to the changes introduced by one's disease, both in the case of its worsening, and in overcoming temporary aggravations.

Chapter 26

Between visible and invisible

Many chronically ill patients have no obvious disability or signs of a disease. To those who do not know them or to those who meet them in moments of relative well-being, they appear as completely normal people. A more careful observation could note a slowness in walking, a certain hindrance in moving, the pallor of the face, strange behaviors such as going to the bathroom often or avoiding taking a bus. However, these are not situations that suggest a constant condition of disease, for the most part they are considered as passing or individual characteristics.

Many times, especially in the past, when I revealed to someone that I have multiple sclerosis, the look on the interlocutor's face appeared to be one of doubt, then the exclamation: "You don't look like you do." These reactions not only highlight the interlocutor's difficulties in dealing with a painful truth, which one would prefer to ignore; they show very well the ambiguous and contradictory existential condition of the chronically ill, where there are aspects of similarity but also of great difference with others.

On the one hand, a person that has a serious and lasting illness is very different from others. On the other hand, they are individuals of which many aspects and moments of their life are in likeness of one another; in general, one also does everything possible to present themselves as normal in social situations of daily life, trying to manifest one's best and avoid activities that may reveal one's limits. In times of worsening or relapse, a patient remains at home or is hospitalized, and only the closest family and friends have the possibility to know of their real condition. Often, as long as it is feasible, a patient may choose vacation periods for therapies and recovery time, hiding out with the excuse of having nothing more than a banal complication such as the flu. After the crisis and relapse, in the eyes of others – the situation is back to normal, but it is not so for a patient.

Appearing like others can be of great help to a patient, since it stimulates one to actively use resources and to give one's all, to avoid rejection or to be considered different. Unfortunately, however, this normality is only in appearance; the disease is always, with its symptoms and its limitations, at any moment ready for a worsening, a relapse, to remind one that you are not completely normal. Then very little is needed to reveal the disease, triggering otherwise hidden symptoms, falling into situations of great suffering. It can be a lit cigarette, the absence of toilets, a broken elevator, a waiting line in an office, the driving of a car in urban traffic, excessive noise, all are examples of normal inconveniences that can be addressed and resolved but for a patient can be insurmountable.

In this sense, the chronically ill person is a testimony of someone who lives in particularly painful situations which, even for healthy people, can be a source of suffering. For this reason, the request for attention to the needs of ill individuals in everyday life is not a presumptuous expression of privilege, on the contrary, it is in the need of a well-being for all in a variety of environments from urban planning to road maintenance, from architecture to means of public transportation, from the accessibility of public offices to that of shops. In this regard, the situation in Italy is particularly negative, especially when compared to that of the countries of central and northern Europe. Both private and public administrations often ignore the needs of ill citizens, and with them those of everyone, since anyone may find themselves in a less comfortable health condition: as we have discussed, there is no definition for "perfect well-being." In this sense, public and private interests seem to believe, sometimes even explicitly, that the ill "must stay at home" so as to not disturb established practices with their needs, which are now so uncritically accepted that they seem completely obvious and indisputable.

Sooner or later throughout the years of a disease, the relapses, frequent and recurring in many chronic pathologies, minimize the moments in which it is possible to blend in with other people and increasingly expand the periods in which one's illness is more seriously unveiled. In these moments, the effects of the disease become public, for example absences from work, up to visible physical manifestations visible to strangers. Thus, it becomes impossible to continue to hide one's condition.

In this regard, the choices of the ill can be very different from when the disease began. There are some patients who immediately make the diagnosis known to everyone – relatives, acquaintances, fellow workers – then there are others who prefer greater reserve; it is an individual process of assessment and choice, which everyone must make in relation to the context in which they live and their personal preferences. But even when greater privacy has been preferred, the moment arrives for everyone when it is no longer possible to hide one's illness. We must be aware that this moment is not without consequences: if it is true that it clarifies and simplifies many relationships, it also exposes the risk of refusal attitudes, exclusions, attempts to take advantage of a condition of weakness (for example, in employment relationships), morbid curiosities and manipulations.

In social life there are precise rules, called "exhibition rules," which govern the expression of our negative emotions. Precisely to avoid contagion and social malaise, even if in a different way from culture to culture, they censor the direct expression of negative emotions, by virtue of a social contract according to which we mutually commit ourselves not to make others suffer with our pain. Outside of specific ritual moments, such as funerals, it is generally considered inappropriate to show one's suffering openly to outsiders, even if Mediterranean cultures allow for greater expressiveness. These rules, necessary for social coexistence, may lead a patient to a state of incommunicability and estrangement from others.

I have experienced several times how difficult it is to answer the simple question "how's it going?" A sincere answer, in fact, often embarrasses the interlocutor, who in reality does not expect a real answer. On the other hand, in many situations, the patient does not have the willingness to clearly disclose their negative feelings, for various reasons: fear of letting go too much, attempting to maintain a positive self-image, distrust of the interlocutor including his/her capacity for understanding. However, a conventional and insincere response can alienate the interlocutor, who in the future will avoid showing interest. This can make a patient experience feelings of falsehood, alienation and inability to communicate. In these cases, it is useful to try to identify people with whom you want to communicate with in a sincere way and maintain a polite detachment with others.

The swing between moments of relative well-being, in which one tries to face the normal tasks of everyday life to recover whatever in work or in family has been left unresolved, and moments in which one's withdrawal from life is almost total, is a source of many difficulties for the patient and their social relationships. It makes planning difficult, not only in the long term but often also in the short term. A patient may have difficulty judging what they are capable of doing, given two opposite errors in assessment: thinking in moments of well-being that they are able to do more than is possible, and planning initiatives that will prove unattainable, or underestimating their concrete possibilities at times of worsening health. Even at work, this difficulty of evaluation can lead to making commitments that one will not be able to fulfill, or, on the contrary, to excessively limit one's actions. Looking at myself, after some mistakes, I learned to not make a decision immediately when a proposal is made, even if it is very simple, until the future: by letting the project settle for a few hours or days, when my limits and possibilities become clear to me, I am then able to give a more realistic response, thus recovering a sense of self-efficacy and normality.

Chapter 27

Solitude

The word "solitude" defines two very different conditions. The first concerns the painful feeling of not being in tune with others, of not having people to talk to, share emotions, share one's intimacy, ask for help. It is that sense of estrangement that can be felt not only in the midst of an anonymous crowd, but also, unfortunately, within the home, amongst people we are familiar with. So, there is nothing worse than the experience of solitude lived in a marriage, if one finds themselves constricted into forced intimacy with a foreign and distant person.

It is quite different to be alone, in the sense of not being in the company of others. It is the solitude of an afternoon spent at home, but also that of a person who lives, by choice or necessity, alone. For some, this solitude is truly definable as blessed, according to the Latin saying "*beata solitudo, sola beatitudo*" ("blessed solitude, only happiness"), while for others it constitutes an unpleasant if not intolerable condition. In our society, solitude is often shunned, even at the cost of inventing and researching situations, such as in a nightclub, where one is physically with others, but nothing significant is communicated and shared, resulting in an experience of solitude as the alienation aforementioned.

The chronically ill person often experiences the first type of loneliness, due to the difficulties of communicating and sharing their feelings with others, even when they are very dear to them. Beyond the differences in temperament between more or less introvert people, the condition of continuous suffering often makes it difficult to express one's moods: not only because speaking can be too tiring, but also because with one's externalizing one is afraid of being burdensome to others, or even because one is afraid of boring them by repeating the same arguments. At the same time, others may fear being intrusive or prying, or have serious difficulty facing negative and persistent spirits. In particular, two opposite reactions can be very painful for a patient: that of those who minimize suffering, both physical and psychological, causing lack of understanding, and that of those who exaggerate, without being of any help, even burdening the patient to reverse the role of who should be providing comfort. Since we cannot expect others to understand our moods and our difficulties if we do not express them explicitly and unambiguously, it is essential that a patient commits effort to communicate as clearly as possible with others: certainly not with everyone, but with those who are important and significant to them.

As for being alone, the situation for the patient can be particularly contradictory. On the one hand, the chronically ill cannot live without others: family members, friends, services are an indispensable presence for one's daily life, sometimes even for the care of their body. Certainly only the help of family and friends allows the patient to survive among the numerous and mostly unmotivated rules that regulate one's relations with health services: in order to successfully untangle oneself from this forest, it is in fact required, paradoxically, to have a lot of time and be in perfect health. At the same time, however, conditions of a disease tend to alienate others: poor mobility limits encounters; tiredness prevents one from frequenting friends and participating in the usual moments marking social life; relapses prevent relationships from being maintained on an ongoing basis; the unpredictability – so accentuated in some pathologies – puts a strain on social relationships, because it does not allow us to keep our commitments.

For all these reasons, a patient risks a progressive impoverishment of their relationships in life, sometimes even isolation, because slowly others get tired of one's refusals and their absences, and the ill become engulfed in the emptiness of an unwanted loneliness, full of anguish. For this reason, it is essential that a patient works actively to maintain relationships with others as much as possible, enhancing their ability to build and maintain social relationships effectively. Fortunately, there are many tools today, such as the telephone and e-mail, which, despite the limitations due to the absence of a direct relationship, permit one to stay in touch with others even without leaving one's home or bed.

On the other hand, a patient, like any other person, also needs their own moments and spaces of solitude. Indeed, sometimes one feels an urgent need to not feel suffocated by the presence, although necessary, of those who often have to invade his or her body sphere, and because one is in a condition of tiredness, pain or malaise makes being with others disturbing (such as listening to their speech, seeing them move around one, being touched, to have to speak). The request of the patient to want to be alone should therefore not always be seen as a refusal by family members or friends, but respected and accepted with equanimity. It can express not only the need for rest, but also the need to have a moment of detachment necessary for personal reflection and to regain one's own sense of separated individuality. Sometimes silence is enough for this purpose, which does not mean refusal or closure, but on the contrary an opportunity to recharge and deepen a patient's sense of being.

Chapter 28

Attachments

The sociability of the human being is expressed in a privileged way given our relationships of affection: from the family of origin, between a couple and their children, from old friends to more recent ones. With these people we establish relationships of attachment, of trust, of sharing, of mutual help, which can also last a lifetime and are not necessarily based on genetic affinity. In the culture of the last century, above all thanks to psychoanalysis, the conviction had spread that there was a primacy of sexuality and that affective relationships derived from it. Studies on attachment for decades have refused and reversed this position, clarifying that emotional relationships are primary and are sought after by the child, whose well-being they base it on, right from his or her entrance into life. It is necessary to remember this because often in our society, so strongly sexualized, it is difficult to grasp the autonomous value of affective relationships. Thus, there is a tendency to confuse attachment with sex, believing that there are no affective ties exempt from the sexual drive, and to believe that the latter is always primary with respect to attachments that descend from it. In fact, the phylogeny of sex and attachments developed differently; in humans, from birth the development of the attachment bond toward, as a rule, the biological mother, has precise innate bases and is primary in respect to the development of sexuality. Throughout life, the ability to give and receive affection is essential to personal fulfillment and identity development.

Situations of attachment in the chronically ill patient can be the most diverse; depending on personal conditions (being married or not, having or not having children) of illness (at what moment of life one is affected by illness and what is its evolution), it is neither possible nor useful to enter into a detailed case study. Considering the enormous diversity of relationships in one's life, chronic disease, whatever it may be, has a very significant impact on the emotional life of a patient, both within family and with friends. In fact, it puts relationships in difficulty: if, on the one hand, some become closer, also because of a patient's need to be helped, on the other, some others may weaken, because a patient lacks the energy and time to devote to relationships and to the activities that go with them. In this way, it is no longer possible to meet friends who live in other cities, since traveling becomes too much, or to engage in the sporting activities once shared with friends during free time. Furthermore, it is not just a few people who have difficulty accepting the reality of a disease and, facing the problems of a patient, they tend to draw back. However, more often than not, a patient does not try to bridge the distance, feeling their uneasiness.

Even the closest affective ties can encounter difficulties, due to the great commitment that is required from both partners in continuing to project their life together, now marked by a disease, creating an imbalance attributable to the conditions of the disease and the needs of the ill. Some situations can be particularly critical. One is that of the patient who is at the same time a parent: being confined to the role of those who need help and are no longer able to be as supportive to their children, this can cultivate feelings of guilt and great suffering (see Part VI). More generally, toward younger people, toward whom we have educational responsibilities, there is often the fear of producing in them anxiety and problems that are too difficult to handle. In reality, any patient still has a lot to give to their children and others: it is enough that they carry out a careful analysis of their limits and possibilities. It is a question of enhancing what can be given and of relying on a communication that is as clear as possible. At other times a patient, fearing that they will no longer be able to build significant affective relationships, or fearing to lose those that they have due to their disease, accepts any behavior from others, even the most unfair and demeaning, in order not to remain alone and delude themselves to receive their affection. Other times, on the contrary, it is a patient themself who uses the disease as a weapon to keep people tied to oneself and force them to provide care. In all these cases, these are problems that are solvable but are not effectively addressed, commonly occurring in healthy couples as well. In attachments, as in every other aspect of one's life, a patient must not give up being the protagonist of their own development, striving to build and maintain the affective relationships one considers significant. It is difficult, much more difficult than in a healthy condition, but not impossible.

In the closest affective relationships, the risk of emotional contagion should not be underestimated, due to the closeness and identification that binds family and friends to the ill person in their daily life and throughout the years of their illness. They therefore also impose the need to learn to understand and share in a differentiated way; for this purpose, moments of psychological and even physical detachment from a patient can help. "Burn out syndrome" is a risk not only for healthcare professionals (for whom this phenomenon depends above all on organizational deficiencies), but also for family members. This name indicates the situation of those who "become extinguished," having burned their resources, no longer being able to help a patient, even causing harm to themselves.

Differentiated empathy allows you not to fall into this situation. It involves the ability not to attribute your emotions to the patient in an egocentric way (the projection of feelings is often the source of great tension between a patient and family members) but to recognize his/her experiences in a differentiated and also sufficiently detached way. Often, with the best of intentions, family members try to help a patient by actually doing what they would do to comfort themselves in a similar situation, without putting themselves in the shoes of the patient. A patient's experience can be profoundly different, meaning the actions of care being provided may not be what is needed. A good empathic relationship is built up over time and with attention, allowing family members and friends to understand a patient and to help them truly, without contagion and without egocentric confusion. If there is an individual developmental task in one's disease, this task also extends to a certain degree to all those involved: family, partner and circle of friends. As close to the patient and eager for their well-being, these participants can play an important role through effective communication, empathetic sharing and the common search for better adaptation.

Among the most terrible experiences for a patient's family and friends is suicide and the fear of it actually happening. As has long been pointed out, suicide is possible only when a person believes they no longer have significant bonds with others. We cannot voluntarily cut ties with life if we live deep ties with other people, whom we love, who love us, whom we suffer in leaving and who in turn will suffer for our death. For many patients, these ties are able to make sense of life even in the most difficult situations. However, it can happen that when the disease worsens, the person voluntarily represses the bonds of affection that bind them to others, because one believes their own conditions of suffering and life are now intolerable and unworthy of a human existence, even in the presence of good affective bonds. These are subjective evaluations, which people close to the patient are often not aware of, therefore can be a cause of enormous suffering for them. However, no one can impose their own meanings and motives for living on another person; one can only help them discover they are of value, even in the most tragic of situations. For this reason, a patient's suicide must be respected as an extreme choice although defeatist, as the ultimate expression of the will to act on one's destiny. This decision that belongs to a person's sense of self-awareness can never be fully explained or traced back to a mechanical game of known causes.

Fully respecting a patient also means accepting the "unknown" of one's final decision, as an independent choice that belongs to the unfathomable depth of their consciousness. Unfortunately, attributions of guilt to family members, based on trivial cause and effect relationships, are frequent both by strangers and family members themselves. However, they are completely out of place and once again represent the attempt to find at all costs a reassuring explanation in front of an event that is a source of immense anguish. At the same time, suicide is certainly always a defeat of life; for this reason, it must be actively contrasted with affection and commitment in helping the patient to live a life worthy of a human being, while facing the intensifying aggravations of disease. The treatment of pain and to repudiate therapeutic obstinacy are indispensable conditions for trying to find meaning together in life even in extreme conditions.

Chapter 29

Work

Through work, people do not only earn a living, thus managing to achieve the economic autonomy indispensable for self-realization. Work also contributes to building the well-being of one's family and community, thus perceiving oneself as a useful person in the history and development of the society one is living in.

As for affective attachments, the situations that every patient must face with regards to work are very different: from the young person who, due to the disease, cannot find a more or less stable job, to the varying difficulties of those who have a job, but are no longer able to do it as before, whether one works independently or as an employee, resulting in the loss of employment or early retirement as the disease progresses. The working problems of a chronically ill patient are often overlooked, with the tendency to anticipate letting a patient go, when they could continue working under certain conditions. The market and work environments today are increasingly characterized by competition and efficiency – often combined with disorganization – which leave no place for those who are not in perfect condition and do not devote their maximum energy to work: there seems to be no middle ground between working at a frenetic pace and not working at all, between perfect functionality and expulsion from the labor market. Again, this condition is difficult not only for the chronically ill, but for many other people, especially women with young children.

It is a short-sighted concept, where society loses important human capital: a patient is in fact a person who in most cases still has a lot to give on the job level, if suitable locations and performance pacing can be found. It is a question of organizational choices (such as part-time or job change) but also, and perhaps above all, one of attitudes. In particular, in the current mythology of competition, it is often forgotten that a group works well, being productive and capable of withstanding external competition, it is also thanks to the cooperation of its members, to mutual attention and not pitting one against the other. It must not be forgotten that cooperation and help have precise biological bases, and that the development of humanity has taken place much more thanks to these capacities than to the overpowering of each other. It also often forgotten that flexibility is the condition for a better adaptation not only for individuals but also for working groups, in which creativity is not the result of unbridled competition; on the contrary, cooperation goes hand in hand with the most flexible and creative solutions. Asking ourselves then, what a patient's contribution may be and seeking a useful place for them on the job, rather than thinking only of the expulsion of this individual is a profit for the organization and not a loss. In most work situations it is possible to identify, with a little flexibility and inventiveness, different activities in which the patient can still continue to usefully engage, without losses for both the individual and the organization.

Unfortunately, a "victim's blame" finds its worst expression in the workplace. Among the most difficult experiences that a patient must face, just when one makes the maximum effort to continue working, is that of being accused of bad will, of disengagement from one's work obligations, or worse yet of taking advantage of the situation, using illness to one's advantage, if not "pretending to be sick" at one's convenience. If it is undeniable that the alternation of periods of presence and absence from work can create difficulties in one's organization, it is equally true that it is possible to find solutions to these problems, without social dependency, if the patient is still considered capable of making a significant contribution, even if in a different way than before.

Very often, after a longer or shorter period, the patient is forced to leave work. In general, this difficult decision is reached through a slow and painful process, which oscillates between moments in which the idea of abandonment appears unacceptable and unfounded, and others in which it appears realistic and acceptable. The fluctuating trend of a disease, with its improvements and relapses, offers a favorable ground for these hesitations: when you are better and go to work you are convinced you can do it and it seems that you cannot live without work, while the relapses force physical change and make the work feel distant even on a psychological level. In fact, a normal defense mechanism makes work become psychologically less relevant when the primary needs of daily life are at stake. Many times have I experienced this back and forth, passing from the belief of being able to continue working to the certainty that it was no longer possible. Sometimes even a single phone call was enough to make me feel again that my work was indispensable. This swing can be very long and exhausting: to be able to leave work without excessive suffering, it is necessary to have established a certain detachment linked to the progress of the disease and to the acceptance of reality, that is, the material impossibility of continuing to work.

Facing the demands of one's work and aggravation of one's disease, an objective analysis of reality needs to be done more than ever, in order to arrive at choices that allow for better adaptation and personal development. Some sufferers make the mistake of fleeing immediately from work even when they could continue, both for lack of employee support in the working environment and for overestimating the objective difficulties of the situation. In these cases, a recovery of self-efficacy is essential, and must concern not only the technical abilities to carry out one's work but even more how to deal with the conflicts and social tensions of the working environment. Opposing this, is the widespread social prejudice, where the ill believe that there can be no personal fulfillment except in work. This conviction leads a patient to insist on continuing to work when there are no longer the objective conditions for doing so, and to experience retirement, or even just a change in the type of work, with strong feelings of failure and uselessness. Many concomitant situations such as economic difficulties and work and family responsibilities, can aggravate one's experiences. Here flexibility is fundamental to search for a helpful adaptation and to make choices that lead to personal development and not to impoverishment. When work is no longer possible in any form, not even reduced or different, it is useful to look for other interests and other forms of social participation, such as volunteering. In any case, the change in work or leaving work entails a profound restructuring of one's identity, self-image, sense of existence, relationships with others, which is always demanding, and sometimes long and very painful. In it there is the concrete possibility of finding one's own active role in the community and in the family, based on one's interests, preferences and possibilities.

Chapter 30

Life and death

To each of us, it does not matter whether one is of faith or not, we can live particular moments feeling our being as infinitesimal and at the same time a feeling of unity, of participation in totality of which we are nonetheless a tiny part. It may be pondering an ancient civilization, reflecting on the evolution of life, reading a piece of poetry, contemplating nature or a work of art, listening to music, meditation. As for me, nothing can give me a greater sense of participation in the universe than contemplating a star-filled sky from a high mountain. Far from any light, thousands of stars become visible and remind me that my existence is part of an ancient and mysterious adventure that started well before the beginning of human life. This contemplation, while making many of the problems I face every day feel small and irrelevant, does not have the effect of diminishing the value of my existence. On the contrary, my human life, limited and fleeting, appears to me as a small piece in the wonderful history of the universe, which I am called to honor, by living my life as best I can in the time and place I have been granted.

Looking at the sky, the sense of wonder is renewed, well expressed by Immanuel Kant's words on the moral law within us and on the starry sky above us – which, at the time, was certainly much more visible and appreciable than today, with the light and atmospheric pollution that veils the view of the sky from the cities. The two experiences are connected, not only because the human mind is the only one, among the living beings on earth, with the capacity to evaluate the splendor of the sky, but also because our thinking mind is united to the matter of that starry sky much more than it appears. The elements that make up the universe are the same as those found in the solar system and on earth, as life originated from them: there is a profound unity between the cosmos and the earth on which we live. In this small part of space, starting from those elements, life has developed, from the simplest to the most complex forms, all closely related. Among these, the human being has developed this potential to be capable of thinking and a sense of self-awareness, that is to say, of reflection on oneself in relation to our surrounding world. Thought is able to act admirably on the world and thanks to the creation of cultural tools – most importantly writing – can overcome the limits of space and time. There is therefore a profound unity between the celestial vault and our thought which contemplates and admires it.

In this unity, even death finds its place. For the biologist, death is a natural part of life: it is the destiny of every living being, which thus falls within the great biological cycle of existence. This biological cycle can only continue on earth through future generations and single deaths after a period of life, for each species cannot go beyond a certain maximum. Even for the scientist, death and life are inextricably linked in the physical and biological world. For the psychologist, the human mind is the highest expression that life has made. The mind, with its thoughts and its creations, arises from the biological functioning of the brain, suffers from its limits and ceases with the degradation of its biological structures. In this sense, the mind does not escape the transience of life. But the psychologist also knows that the human mind radically rejects the idea of death, which it finds unacceptable and against which it develops thoughts of transcendence and immortality.

The human mind, even when, with the most advanced part of its thought, comes to accept the naturalness of death, in reality it rebels deeply against it and finds it intolerable. Prehistoric evidence indicates that our ancestors always buried their dead. The burial and funeral items symbolize a hope in a world beyond, where they may continue living together with loved ones, even together with things and animals. These burials are testimony to both the profound refusal of death that has always accompanied human beings, and the strong emotional bond with loved ones. It is the attachment to loved ones and the refusal of their death, perhaps even more than our own, that establishes the hope that life does not end with death and can continue beyond it.

Contrary to what many believe, an immanent vision of life does not in itself lead to contempt for life in general, nor contempt for human life in particular, including the overpowering of other human beings. On the contrary, it can lead to greater attention to what we do toward others and the world, in the brief period in which our existence unfolds on this planet. The time of our life is limited and there are no other possibilities for redemption; life is therefore a great responsibility, playing our best hand, toward others, other living forms to which we are related, future generations, the physical world that hosts us from which life was born. The predisposition to positive sociality – that is, to cooperation, altruism, attachment, to love – is inscribed among the biological possibilities of the human being as well as aggression and destructiveness. If it is up to culture to choose to favor the development of one or the other, it is the prerogative of each individual to decide consciously and responsibly, in small and large alternatives of existence, which type of social relationship with others to engage in.

Such a view of life does not inevitably lead to despair. On the contrary, it can lead to an acceptance of existence as part of a whole that flows for each of us along a transcendent time, an acceptance from which derives a greater sense of responsibility toward that small piece of life that is expressing itself through us. The need to express one's existence in the best way can then be an element of strength in disease. The patient, in fact, can seek a better adaptation and personal development not only in view of greater well-being, as we have addressed since the beginning of this book, but also because of the need to live as fully as possible with the splendid wealth, albeit imperfect and painful, which has been given to us.

Whatever one's outlook on life is, for the ill, the thought of death is much closer than it is for the majority of people. As a disease progresses, the patient can experience a condition of marked conflict: on the one hand, wanting death to end their suffering, on the other, fearing it because, for anyone, death is always an unacceptable reality. What the elderly and the sick today declare to fear most, in the Western world, is not so much death itself as the poor conditions in which life is lived, sometimes long lasting before death. The pain, the dependence, the physical and intellectual decay, the weighing upon others, are considered much more intolerable than death itself. Here we approach a theme that is taboo for contemporary culture, apparently so open and free, in which nevertheless removes death and all that accompanies it, much more than many cultures of the past. The weakening of religious sentiment was not countered by the development of a secular acceptance of death. On the contrary, the refusal of death, its denial, subtraction from sight, confinement in technological spaces devoid of human relations have increased. In particular, health workers see their own defeat in death and deny it even more than other people; very often they confuse the extension of the vegetative life with the extension of a life endowed with meaning. This is what patients fear: the therapeutic obstinacy, the pain and the conditions in which perhaps the last moments of their existence will be lived. In Western society, the ever greater and more invasive power of health systems appears objective, there is much work to be done to recover the right of every person to die in humane conditions. Therapeutic obstinacy protects only those who practice such implementation, because then they are reassured that they have done everything possible to keep the patient alive, without asking themselves if this was really the life that the patient would have wanted to lead in their last days. Respect, on the other hand, stems from overcoming egocentric interests and then recognizing that the sense of a patient's life, even in their last moments, must be found and realized together.

Part VI

We need to recognize our own deficiencies, including physical ones; a need to accept that we can no longer be for another as we would like.

We need to be always willing to reexamine our lives, to begin again everything in a different place.

Chapter 31

Diagnosis
Confronting the truth

Receiving the diagnosis of chronic disease is a serious blow. Our mind is facing an event that is too new, too different, too negative, which shatters our habitual way of looking at life and the future. In the immediate future, as often happens in the face of violent and unexpected negative events, many people experience a sense of unreality and the diagnosis is not accepted as a true fact: "It is not possible, I cannot believe it." This sense of incredulity can lead, if even for a short time, to question the diagnosis itself: "It can't be, until the day before yesterday I was fine, I'm young, there is no illness in the family, the doctor is wrong."

These are immediate and short-lived defense reactions, which are not to be considered pathological. It takes time to get to know the prospect of having a disease that will never abandon us for life, and for which there are currently no definitive treatments that allow us to talk about healing and not just temporary remissions. I am not talking here about the acceptance of the disease – this is a slow and rocky process, composed of reoccurring crises, even for those who have been ill for many years. I speak of the previous phase, immediately following the diagnosis: realizing that the diagnosis is true, that this is our reality, not only today but for the rest of our lives.

Paradoxically, the diagnosis can also be experienced with relief, at least temporarily, by those who for some time, even for years, were confronted with strange ailments that could not be explained. These people often see various specialists without being able to obtain a clear diagnosis. No one can understand what is happening to them and often they experience the unpleasant feeling of being considered an imaginary patient, or at least strange – not believable, describing baffling exaggerated symptoms, again that no one can trace to a specific disease. Consequently, considering the number of doctors who are not able to give a diagnosis, means that the disease simply does not exist, except in the ill person's imagination and fears. For this reason, finally having a diagnosis can, in some cases, can be almost a relief: at least one is recognized in one's own physical suffering and one knows what to fight against.

This condition is less frequent today than in the past, because for many pathologies, including multiple sclerosis, new diagnostic techniques allow diagnosis to be made faster. More generally, having a clear diagnosis in a short time is important not only in setting up a therapy (even if it is not comprehensive) to relieve some physical symptoms but for psychological reasons as well. The human mind fears a danger it does not know and cannot identify, for this one's anxiety about the uncertainty of a diagnosis is a stress factor not to be underestimated. This is why the phrase a doctor said to me one day, "What is the use of complaining about not having had the diagnosis early if there is no cure?" is senseless.

After the first brief phase of unreality and disbelief, the confrontation with the diagnosis, now recognized as real, provokes strong emotions: fear for the future ("what will become of me?"), anger at the adverse fate that has struck ("why me?"), feeling of being victim of an injustice ("with all that I have already suffered in my life ..."), sadness to the point of depression. Anger can turn against doctors, who are honestly clarifying the chronic nature of the disease, as it is. In multiple sclerosis, in particular, many respond angrily to the definition of this disease as "neurodegenerative demyelinating," which they find offensive: since they cannot attack the disease, they attack the person giving the diagnosis. However, it is unfortunately true that the way in which a diagnosis is communicated can be harsh and abrupt, too technical and devoid of empathy, that is, void of consideration and participation for a patient's anguish. Giving a diagnosis of this type requires a suitable place (certainly not the corridor!) and sufficient time, to allow listening and dialogue, with a genuine attitude of participation. Although, it must be remembered that in any case it is the duty of a doctor to not tell lies, just as it is the right of a patient to demand the truth. Lies can calm anxiety for a moment, but the illusions that they cultivate, precisely because they are without foundation, cannot promote positive reactions in a patient with a disease that will accompany them forever. Not to mention that illusions can lead a patient to falling into the hands of unscrupulous, unskilled individuals. The Italian chronicle of recent years is unfortunately full of examples of this type.

Knowledge of the truth about the diagnosis is therefore indispensable. I stress this because it still happens today to find family members – parents, but not only them – who would like to keep the person concerned in the dark about the diagnosis. In addition to being impossible for fundamental legal obligations toward an adult, this masquerade translates into a betrayal of the trust relationship that must exist between people linked by bonds of affection. For this, a patient when the diagnosis has been hidden from them even for a short time, feels betrayed. Although motivated consciously by a desire to protect, pretending to hide a diagnosis sometimes conceals a desire for control, in a situation of inequality between family members; more often, however, it hides the personal difficulty of the family members, above all parents, to face what is also a very difficult truth for them to accept. But the experience of betrayal also concerns the doctor: as we have seen, chronic disease requires lasting collaboration that can only be achieved if a patient is aware of the diagnosis and can fully trust the sincerity of the doctor.

Immediately after a diagnosis, some people shut themselves up and do not admit to having negative feelings, to appear serene at all costs, often in order not to burden family members. Many others still do not want to talk about their disease and much less face those who have been affected. I remember well the reaction I had in the early days after my diagnosis when I saw on the television a discussion about multiple sclerosis. My heart pounded immediately; I felt the desire to listen carefully, to find out more, but at the same time I wanted to flee, run away, go away, not hear anything, turn the television off – this happened more than once. Visits to the center where I was being treated were also a source of tension. I encountered people with serious and visible damage, and thought with anguish: "Is this my future – when will it arrive?" Lying on the bed with an IV in my vein, I listened to the stories of a neighbor as fear invaded me: "What will my destiny be? How will I cope in everyday life? Will I still be able to write?"

Chapter 32

"I want to do it on my own"

Immediately after one's diagnosis every patient experiences a tangle of negative emotions and strong defensive reactions, completely understandable and in many ways inevitable; however, this is also very dangerous and therefore must diminish over time. It is dangerous because it adds to a disease the aggravation of suffering that could be avoided or reduced, and because an ill person risks being imprisoned in a cage that prevents them from addressing the demanding life challenge facing them, now and for always. To avoid this it is important to intervene immediately after one's diagnosis with psychological help, for two main purposes: first, to provide the ill person with the tools necessary to avoid becoming overwhelmed by negative feelings and mistaken defensive reactions; second, to teach how to deal with disease by mobilizing one's best personal resources.

I emphasize that the need for psychological help does not derive from the problematic nature of a person, but from the significant difficulties posed by a chronic disease that will accompany them throughout their life, therefore requiring a continuum of self-restructuring one's identity, objectives and goals, and how to achieve them. Disease, as we have seen, is a challenge to personal development and self-realization. It is therefore necessary to look at an ill person not from a psychopathological point of view, as unfortunately still prevails frequently, but from a personal development perspective (see Part I); in this dynamic proactive vision, attention must be focused on the best ways to face the grueling challenges posed by illness. This positive vision must be present in doctors and health personnel, but also by the ill person themselves; from the moment that one's life is now accompanied by illness, it is a question of living this life to the fullest, even if with illness: living, not surviving.

The experience of these years has confirmed to me that many people have enormous personal resources, which they manage to mobilize admirably and with extraordinary strength of soul. This is not, however, a good reason to refuse specialist help, which allows you to suffer less, waste less time, quickly learning the best ways to manage illness in everyday life. Concretely, it is about offering everyone the opportunity for psychological support. I know very well the prejudices toward the usefulness of resorting to psychology are numerous; they continue to deny many people opportunities that provide effective chronic disease coping methods. These prejudices involve both those affected by the disease and, not infrequently, the health workers themselves, who indirectly contribute to the belief that a psychologist deals only with psycho-pathological conditions. Consequently, a patient often refuses psychological support because it seems to them this refers only to those who are crazy, or at least strange, incapable or to failure, conditions in which they do not recognize in themselves and actually fear. Instead, it is essential to move to a dynamic and proactive vision, which looks at the demanding challenges posed to personal fulfillment by illness and the best ways to tackle them.

There is therefore no pathological or problematic person to cure, but a chronic disease that poses significant obstacles upon the ill, to be confronted with the best personal resources which psychological intervention helps to discover and mobilize. In short, it is a matter of considering the use of a psychologist as an opportunity to optimize one's growth path: it is always the person who acts, without delegation or dependence, but with greater tools to cope with one's life every day. Psychological help makes it possible to activate more resources in facing the different and relevant difficulties that disease gradually poses. For this it is a mistake to say "I can do it on my own," pitting this statement against seeking help. Even with psychological help, in fact, it is always us who "do it on our own" because no one can be us in everyday life.

After the diagnosis, we often find ourselves in a paradoxical situation: people are in the point in which they need more psychological help to face the problems raised by a disease, but at the same time easily reject it. In fact, escape and denial mechanisms are frequent, which lead to not wanting to talk about one's disease or engaging with anything that can remind them of it. For this reason, it is important that psychological assistance is offered by specialist centers as a normal treatment option, like pharmacological therapies; as long as it remains something rare, it will never be considered a normal opportunity to be seized. Today this happens very sporadically in Italy, causing the loss of resources, time and well-being, as well as the abandonment of some medical therapies. It continues with health specialists, a conception that the psyche is as an entity separate from the body, as if mind and brain were not strictly dependent on each other in the unity of a person.

To overcome this situation, for some years now, I have been the scientific director of a group psychological intervention for people who have had the diagnosis of multiple sclerosis for at least three years.[1] It was decided it was best to carry out this activity outside the hospital context, which often arouses feelings of anxiety and evokes negative experiences. Indeed, an environment of particular architectural and naturalistic beauty was chosen, considered as potentially more enticing for participants and promoting a positive disposition within them, given a context normally used by everyone for cultural activities.

This ten-year experience, of which the effectiveness has been verified and is continuously subject to evaluation (see Bibliography), has confirmed the issues identified in the previous chapters are central points for a chronically ill patient. In fact, one must learn to live with a disease that requires a search for worthy objectives compatible with its limits, proficient in giving meaning to one's life and allowing the realization of one's identity; at the same time an ill person must learn to use the best strategies to effectively achieve identified objectives. One also needs to learn to control negative emotions, to promote positive ones, as well as to implement good communication both with family members and with healthcare personnel.

From this positive experience a double invitation arises. First of all, so that ill people do not refuse to face life's complexities posed by a disease, seek and accept psychological help. There is no shame in this! On the contrary, it is a sign of intelligence and care for yourself and the people you love. But knowingly, this invitation is at the same time also a strong reprimand, as it is also addressed to the public health, which continues to be guilty of neglecting the psychological aspects of health care (as if this is not within their competence and interest), not fully addressing the well-being of ill people. In Italy there is a serious cultural delay in this regard; there is no longer any justification for this absence of care. Today, there are well-known and scientifically founded ways to offer opportunities to better cope with disease, and therefore offering a better life with illness.

Note

1 The project is the result of the collaboration between the Cosso Foundation (San Secondo di Pinerolo, Turin), the Department of Psychology of the University of Turin and the Cresm (Multiple Sclerosis Regional Center) of the hospital-university "S. Luigi Gonzaga" of Orbassano (Turin).

Chapter 33

Being ill in the Internet age

If some people, after being diagnosed, do not want to hear about their disease, others try in every way to find information about it, often on their own. This urgency responds to a fundamental need of the human mind: knowing helps to live the reality that threatens us – chronic illness is certainly a serious threat. Since we are talking about currently incurable diseases, it is completely normal for a person to seek information especially on possible new therapies, that is, on what could perhaps reduce the chronicity of their condition. Sometimes those around a patient, even in the healthcare world, do not understand this behavior and comment: "What is the use of inquiring about the disease, if there are no resolutive therapies? What do patients do with this information, which they are often unable to evaluate? Isn't this what doctors are for?" These observations do not capture an important aspect of the human mind, which lives with greater anxiety for what it does not know, which appears obscure, confused or ambiguous. And since the cognitive aspects are strictly connected to the emotional ones, having adequate information and knowledge also helps one to feel more in control of oneself, more confident, more capable of coping with one's disease.

But there is not only this, which, however, would already be a lot. Much knowledge, for example about what in daily life can help you feel better or the opposite make you feel worse, is essential for greater well-being. So, this is not unnecessary knowledge; on the contrary, even with a non-curable disease, being able to know and manage one's symptoms consents to living better. These symptoms, in everyday life, can be recognized and addressed with the right strategies only by a patient who has adequate knowledge: a condition of ignorance does not allow you to do this. Concretely, knowledge allows one to act in an adequate way, therefore, feeling far more capable of dominating the disease: not in an illusory way, but thanks to a greater feeling of effectiveness in exercising control over its symptoms. Just think of the information on strategies concerning fatigue management, one of the most pervasive, unrecognized and invisible disabilities that many patients, not only of multiple sclerosis, have to face daily. Even if the disease reminds us every day that it is not humanly possible to "have everything under control," as many today in our society have the illusion of doing, being able to improve this control is of great help.

Knowledge also helps to establish a better collaborative relationship with doctors and healthcare personnel. This is indispensable in managing a disease that lasts over time and where a patient must absolutely have an active and not passive role, such as it was with the old paternalistic model. It is therefore first and foremost the duty of physicians and health personnel to provide good information and transmit adequate knowledge, being clear that the information does not coincide with knowledge. The latter is the organization of information – which in itself has separate elements – in a structured framework capable of relating them and giving them meaning, explaining their connections. It is therefore up to the healthcare staff to give scientifically based knowledge and information, not being afraid to honestly recognize if knowledge is not present or is lacking, to disclose if the information is not entirely certain: in chronic disease, by definition, this is often verifiable.

The work of health education continues to be limited in Italy, as well as in many other countries. Lack of time is often invoked; in reality, a misinformed patient, who asks a thousand times for clarification or who does not understand their prescriptions well, is really wasting time, meanwhile running the risk of damage and complications. These are all situations that could be spared if sufficient space and time were devoted to explaining essential aspects to a patient: for example, what is known about the disease, what therapies are available, what criteria is used for trying one therapy over another, how should a selected therapy be carried out, just to name a few. Experience confirms that providing knowledge and information as a group to several ill people is the best way not only to save time, but also to help people learn. In fact, one person's questions prompt additional questions, consequently one learns efficiently and better. Where this has been done, the results have always been positive. This educational activity must not be sporadic but continuous and must be included in the normal activities of a specialist center that deals with chronic disease. Where this does not exist, the ill have the right to ask for it.

Today there is one more reason why it is imperative that therapists provide information of good scientific quality on the disease they are working with given the pervasive presence of the Internet and social networks. Not too long ago, access was limited to a few people, today almost everyone, and not just young people, "go on the Internet" to look for information. Unfortunately, in this immense universe, quality knowledge and information are not only rare, but certainly far less in number than those devoid of any scientific value; above all it is necessary to have the criteria to be selective, so as not to be overwhelmed by the opinions of pseudo-experts. In concrete terms, this means being able to recognize reliable sites, by confirming they are the expression of recognized scientific institutions, such as universities or research centers, or associations that have scientific committees. There are many blogs where people who are completely lacking in scientific skills promote themselves as experts, and confidently offer advice and peremptory prescriptions. Ill people, in their feverish search for information, easily become victims of this. These bloggers are not only driven by narcissistic self-exhibition, but also, above all, by precise commercial interests more or less hidden.

At the same time, there are numerous sites that present themselves in an attractive and authoritative way, but which are completely devoid of scientific credentials and whose proposals are solely commercial. Many forums are also created, responding to the need for comparison – protected by anonymity – meaning those who have their own disease. Not all of them are managed by serious organizations that control their contents; this is where it is often possible to find indications and advice completely without foundation; not to mention that another person's experience with a certain drug says nothing about the effect that the latter can have on someone else.

A negative trait that characterizes forums, when they are not controlled, is the manifestation of aggression: from the inappropriate joke to the malicious criticism, from the mild irony to sarcasm and open verbal aggression. Unfortunately, verbal aggression is a trait common to all social networks: it is not an accessory, but derives from their intrinsic characteristics. The self-styled "social" in fact favors the display of self and the manifestation of the most primitive emotional reactions – beginning with aggression – without inhibitions and without taking into account the other. In virtual communication there is no face-to-face meeting with other people: the only true way of living human sociality, for which we are biologically predisposed. Only personal encounters favor sharing and empathy, that is, the ability to put yourself in another person's shoes, limiting aggressive responses. Social networks activate the most primitive parts of the human brain and provoke impulsive and uncontrolled emotional reactions, which spread among multiple users, divided into opposing groups, with a crescendo of automatic responses, devoid of critical evaluation and reflection. This primitive reactivity is aggravated by anonymity, which allows you to express yourself aggressively without paying for the social consequences, as it happens in real life. For today, it is becoming increasingly clear that the so-called social networks abuse this definition; in reality they are very "*asocial*," since they exploit for their own purposes, especially economic ones, our natural social tendency, but actually prevent us from living a true human sociality, which is the only real one, face to face with our beings.

Virtual tools and networks certainly have the great advantage of allowing a patient who has difficulty in moving, or lives in peripheral places, to get in touch with other people or specialists. To meet these needs, sites and social networks dedicated to various chronic diseases have been created in recent years, managed by university and research centers or by associations that give guarantees of seriousness; they are not only giving information, but also comparing experiences and connecting ill individuals with one another.

We must never forget, however, that human relationships are such only when they take place in real life. Consequently, virtual instruments are not in themselves an antidote to isolation, but on the contrary they can accentuate it, becoming a substitute or an escape from real life: virtual connection and real isolation are unfortunately an increasingly frequent combination. An ill person, even more than a healthy one, needs to interact with real people: just think of their greater need for substantial help. Therefore, it is always necessary to ask oneself whether frequenting the various sites and networks, even if of verifiable quality, helps to promote real life by enriching one's social network, or if on the contrary does it impoverish it; only in the first case is it useful. Everyone should ask themselves the following questions, answer them sincerely and act accordingly: Does the time I dedicate to social networks have positive effects on my concrete relationships with others? Or is it taking time away from my real-life relationships? Could I use it better in direct relationships? Does it distract me from face-to-face relationships? Does it take me away from the people I am closest to? Does it distract me from other interests? Does it steal hours from sleep?

Another aspect valued highly on all social networks is the sharing of one's experiences with other people. However, it is critical not to fall into the error of considering it enough to express one's own experiences, feelings and emotions to be able to feel better; however useful, this does not guarantee greater awareness of what you are experiencing and consequently does not in itself allow you to find the best ways to deal with the various situations posed by your disease. Although the experience of others is useful to provide a different point of view to reflect on, one should remember that it cannot be applied as it is to another person; not to mention frequent misunderstandings. Only the mediation of an expert can assist in making it possible to understand the meaning of a certain experience and find the best strategies for dealing with a disease. For this reason, sharing on social networks can in no way replace psychological work – individual and group – to learn how to live better even with a chronic disease.

Chapter 34

And life goes on

Chronic disease lasts a lifetime and therefore accompanies people in various phases of existence through decades: changes due to biological modifications (such as menopause), choices that are made (for example, marriage), to an unexpected negative event (an accident) or on a positive note (a job promotion). Being ill is so closely and inextricably intertwined with the continuation of existence, gradually posing new demands and new tasks. For all people, the significant objectives of life change over time and identity is continually reorganized, consequently the goals capable of providing a sense of achievement and the strategies suitable for achieving them evolve; but for the ill, this evolution through the years of existence is accompanied with the unfolding progression of one's disease. As a result, the required readjustments are ongoing and far more relevant.

If in the early days after diagnosis one's attention is more concentrated on the disease, gradually it is no longer their primary focus and patients begin to take into consideration the other situations that the continuation of existence proposes. So, a young man not only wonders about his future with his disease, but finds himself having to decide what job to do, whether to get married or live together, whether to have children. For a young woman, in particular, an important choice concerns possible maternity, a decision that must be taken within a time span delimited by the so-called biological clock, more pressing in females than in males.

These are questions that concern all young people and adults, but for an ill person they acquire particular importance, precisely for the intertwining of life with the course of disease. In multiple sclerosis, specifically, fear of the future – especially of severe disability – can prevent you from making important choices for self-realization and autonomy, such as ending your studies, going to live on your own, cultivating a love. As I have learned painfully over the years, fear is a bad adviser, because it leads us to see the future in a negative and distorted way, anticipating situations that in reality very often will not occur. There is the looming risk of self-limiting one's prospects, excluding life choices that are within our reach, or making others that are dictated only by fear of the future. To use everyday language, one must not "have one's legs cut out from underneath" before the illness does it – which, moreover, perhaps will never cut them. But at the same time, we must not pretend that there is no disease. It is therefore essential to look at your situation with great realism, with the help of specialists, without a sense of omnipotence but also without fear, in this challenging balance one may find the comparison with others most helpful.

It is required of an ill person to have the arduous capacity to tolerate uncertainty and ambiguity: if for each person the future is by definition unknowable, it is even more so for those who are ill. Our mind struggles to endure indeterminacy and even more to reason in terms of probability. Just think of the success of the weather forecast, tools that we turn to with great interest because they allow us to know something about the future, reducing uncertainty, but which at the same time are often interpreted not for what they are, that is, as probabilistic assessments with a margin of error, but as certain truths; hence the disappointment and anger when they do not come true. We must be aware that chronic disease never allows a certain prediction. In multiple sclerosis, in particular, the uncertainty about the evolution of the disease is vast, due to its unpredictability and its progression through relapses and remissions, particularly in the early phase. No one can therefore know for sure what will happen through the years and what will be the evolution of the disease. On one occasion, when asking my naive questions about the future, a neurologist replied: "I don't have a crystal ball," meaning that it is not within the possibilities of medical science to give a certain answer. And since a crystal ball does not exist, uncertainty about one's future must be accepted: another aspect of our limited human condition, which can only rely on probabilistic assessments, both in health and, to an even greater extent, in illness.

In the various moments of life, for each person, and even more for the ill, both the objectives that give meaning and fulfillment to existence change (consequently allowing tangible realization of one's identity), together with the strategies that allow them to be achieved. It is a complex process, which must be continuously reviewed through the years combined with the evolution of one's disease: the objectives, satisfactions and ways of acting that were going well a few years before must be reconsidered and modified. When a young person receives a diagnosis, it is a question of imagining one's own future with the disease and consequently setting goals that take into account its existence. This does not mean giving up hope for the future, but redefining one's plans: work, affections, motherhood and fatherhood pose themselves as important challenges at this age. In adults and maturity, a person often loses the possibility of continuing to realize oneself in areas important for one's identity, such as work or certain social relationships. It is therefore a matter of accepting the loss and redefining one's significant objectives and identity, in a never-ending process. In late maturity and even more in advanced age, a person must face not only their disease but also the greater restrictions due to age, and this entails a double effort. In reality, the chronically ill are forced much earlier and to a much greater extent, to do what each person has to do upon aging: redefine their goals, find new reasons to feel fulfilled, change ways to achieve their goals. Meaning, the chronically ill patient, on the one hand, finds themselves in greater difficulty because added to the physical constraints of their disease are those of aging; on the other hand, they may be able to better face the limitations of advanced age, for it is not new to them to clash with restraint.

As we have said, the goal of this commitment is to live one's life well despite disease, realizing intimately that the best possible way is to live, not to survive. It may happen that "what it takes" to do this is not recognized by those around a patient and that the daily effort behind a patient's achievements is undervalued. Thus, a woman who is struggling with motherhood can be told: "Also you had a son and raised him, like others; therefore, your illness is not so serious." Or: "You still work, so you can't complain." Sometimes these thoughts do not translate into words, but are evident from the attitude and the set of discourses that underestimate the continuous commitment behind these victories. In short, the idea is still widespread (mostly unconsciously) that the ill must "act like an ill person" and should be immediately recognizable as such, as should the acute patients. Regardless, as chronically ill people try to live as best they can through the years, their suffering is underestimated.

Unfortunately, these attitudes are not limited to the private environment, but also concern the social and working environment. For example, it is very difficult for people with chronic disease to be able to travel, and even more to continue working under conditions that are not taking into account their limitations. As chronic disease is on the rise, these problems need to be addressed more decisively than has been the case so far. Unfortunately, many social and working contexts require optimal efficiency, with time, rhythms and methods that can often put those who are healthy in difficulty, hence, completely prohibitive for those who are ill. For this reason, once again, it should be underscored that greater attention to the needs of the ill is not a privilege for the few, but a help for everyone, healthy and ill, young and old, in accepting the boundaries that characterize the human condition.

Chapter 35

Parents and children

In recent years, many chronic diseases have been diagnosed not only in less time, but also at an earlier age. The new technical instruments available to medicine today make it possible to correctly frame isolated episodes, which a few decades ago were without explanation; this fact is positive, because it allows earlier and more targeted therapeutic interventions, although unfortunately not conclusive. For multiple sclerosis, in particular, a young person may be diagnosed, sometimes even an adolescent, still engaged in institutional education and living at home. These are young people who are in the transition phase between dependence on their family and adult autonomy. As is known, this phase is longer in Western society, so much so that it is difficult to say when it ends, and in Italy it is, for various reasons, particularly prolonged. The difficulties in facing this phase are even greater for adolescents and young people who find themselves in a condition of chronic disease early on.

Young age is generally characterized by an optimistic attitude and amazing energy beyond that of an adult; adults are more marked by negative experiences already made and by the inevitable defeats already suffered. However, young people, if on the one hand they possess important resources to address their disease with positive determination, on the other hand they present very often fragility and uncertainties, linked to inexperience and the many fears with which they look to their future, which with disease appears even more uncertain. They cannot count, like the adult, on achievements already realized – for example, romantic attachments and work – their disease places a heavy mortgage on their future, to which they are just embarking on with enthusiasm but also with inescapable trepidation.

In this situation, the relationship with one's family of origin, with whom these young people are still living, can be particularly problematic, especially with their parents. Parents are also experiencing strong negative emotions, filled with fears, anger, guilt, including unfulfilled expectations. The most difficult aspect for parents is to accompany their ill child in the search for their autonomy from the family, to live their own love and working life. It is normal for a parent to want to protect their children; when a child is ill, that desire is, of course, still greater. However understandable, this protective attitude risks keeping a child dependent as if they are still a child. But the ill child is now a young man, or a young woman, who is becoming an adult, meaning the task of the parent is to help them make this transition in the best way, at the same time in full consideration of their disease. The risk too, is when parents project their fears onto their children, imagining for them a bubble-wrapped protected life, very different from how children imagine it for themselves.

A difficult situation, for which there are no "easy recipes" on behavior, since the concrete situations of illness that a young person experiences are all very different. Beginning with a number of questions: How to behave when planning a job away from home, or a study trip abroad, or simply a vacation with friends? What to do when a son or daughter wants to live alone? It is asked of the parent of an ill child, even more than a child in a healthy condition, to stop looking at the future of their children through their own eyes, that is, with a vision of evaluations, hopes and fears. It is a matter of accepting that a child's life is in their hands, yet at the same time, as a parent, being available for help. This is what the child must always feel: that parents are there and can be counted on, but this does not translate into making decisions for them. If it is true that adolescence and youth are a joint path, which affects not only children who grow up and begin to live life independently, but also the parents who accompany them and gradually let them go, this is even more true when a child is ill. For this reason, the positive attitude of parents is a decisive element in helping children to live in the best possible way, inclusive of their illness; meaning establishing achievable goals and learning ways to achieve them, because only a life full of meaning can establish one's identity and sense of fulfillment.

In some families, it is not a child but the parent who has a chronic disease. Often in these cases the parent does not reveal their illness to children, especially if they are small, in the belief that a child cannot understand and that they become fearful of it. We are under the illusion that the silence of adults erases the thought of illness from the minds of children and keeps them more serene. It is not so. Psychology and experience teach that remaining silent with children, and even more with children who are now adolescents, worsens their anxieties and gives them the painful feeling that there are secrets that they are not involved in. These are negative feelings that undermine safety and trust in parents. Unknown realities are more frightful than those that are known, because the dominion of thought and speech can be exercised over them: fears are reduced if you can talk about them and share them, an indispensable condition for developing adequate defenses.

It should be emphasized that children – an aspect often underestimated by adults – are able to grasp with acute perspicacity the uncertainties and embarrassments in the responses of adults, as well as being able to notice in everyday life different behaviors that they may not understand, compounding the risk of formulating their own far more frightening explanations. So a boy can conclude that the father is an addict because he has found a drug hidden in the refrigerator, or a girl can believe that her mother will die because of her frequent visits to a hospital, or even think that her mother does not love her because she is too tired when asked to play together. In this regard, it should be remembered that children think in an egocentric way and therefore tend to report everything that happens. Consequently, in a way completely incomprehensible to an adult, they may think of themselves as the cause of their parent's illness or relapse, establishing cause-effect relationships on situations close in time (such as a child misbehavior and a worsening of the parent symptoms) that do not have any real connection at all.

The truth must therefore always be told to children, with simplicity and by giving essential and useful information for daily life, in the awareness that silence is often an excuse to protect oneself more than children. With younger children you can resort to the help of a fairy tale, which allows you to start the dialogue through metaphors and indirectly. This dialogue will continue over the years, with the raising of children, along with the modification of their cognitive and emotional abilities; parents will return to this topic many times in order to clarify any doubts, to bring out the fears and misinterpretations a child may have (for example, fatigue may be interpreted as lack of interest and lack of affection). The message to be given is that the father or mother has a disease that requires special treatment and attention, but that this does not endanger their life and the serenity of the family; the purpose being is to teach children how to deal effectively with critical situations and the necessary adjustments in daily life that illness requires. A positive attitude, which underlines and brings to the forefront the profoundly joyful aspects of family life, and not only what disease removes or limits, this allows you not to cage your children in a lived experience of pessimism, negativity and suffering.

Many parents claim their most important reason for living is for their children, which helps them to move forward with determination. However, through the years, it is necessary to be vigilant about this concept, as it can lead to keeping a child close to the ill parent in an excessive way for far too long, preventing a child's gradual conquest of autonomy. A good parent must be able to let their children go their own way as they grow older, and this rule also applies to an ill parent. Children should not be placed in a position to feel guilty if they try to fulfill themselves and have an independent life outside their family of origin.

Another important aspect to consider is the development of relational skills. In this regard, it is a common observation that the children of ill parents generally show a greater development of empathy and a strong sense of responsibility; however, this increased sensitivity, which is positive in itself, must not become an unsustainable burden for their age. It is always up to the parent to protect and educate a child, not vice versa. Living in mutual exchange and enrichment means walking on a common path of growth between parents and children, but where the educational responsibility always falls on the adult.

Bibliography

The literature on the diverse arguments discussed is extensive, including many specialized texts and numerous journals, while the various manuals of psychology available on the market (of development, general, social, community and health) introduce basic concepts. This bibliography limits itself to mentioning just a small number of texts, taken from the ample amount of literature on various arguments that are considered in this book, chosen because of their particular significance or accessibility. The texts are grouped by part even though many of them are cross-cutting.

Part I

On development, adaptation and individual action

Baltes P. B., Lindenberger U., Staudinger U. M. (1998). Life-span theory in developmental psychology. In: W. Damon, R. M. Lerner (Eds.), *Handbook of child psychology*. Vol I. *Theoretical models of human development* (pp. 1029–1144). New York: Wiley.

Bonino S. (2001). I nodi teorici attuali. In: A. Fonzi (Ed.), *Manuale di psicologia dello sviluppo* (pp. 43–79). Firenze: Giunti.

Bonino S. (Ed., 2002). *Dizionario di psicologia dello sviluppo*. Torino: Einaudi.

Brandstädter J. (1998). Action perspectives on human development. In: W. Damon, R. M. Lerner (Eds.), *Handbook of child psychology*. Vol I. *Theoretical models of human development* (pp. 807–863). New York: Wiley.

Ford D. H., Lerner R. M. (1992). *Developmental system theory*. Thousand Oaks: Sage.

Hendry L. B., Kloep M. (2002). *Lifespan development. Resources, challenges and risks*. London: Thomson Learning.

Laborit H. (1987). *Dieu ne joue pas aux dés*. Paris: Grasset & Fasquelle.

Lerner R. M. (1998). Theories of human development: Contemporary perspectives. In: W. Damon, R. M. Lerner (Eds.), *Handbook of child psychology. Theoretical models of human development* (pp. 1–24). New York: Wiley.

Piaget J. (1975). L'équilibration des structures cognitives. In: *Etudes d'épistémologie génétique*, vol. XXXIII. Paris: PUF.

Rutter M., Rutter M. (1993). *Developing minds. Change and continuity across the lifespan.* London: Penguin Books.

Silbereisen R. K., Eyferth K., Rudinger E. (1986). *Development as action in context.* Berlin: Springer-Verlag.

Van Geert P. (1994). *Dynamic systems of developments. Change between order and chaos.* New York: Harvester.

Werner H. (1957). *Comparative psychology of mental development.* New York: International Universities Press.

On memory and development of higher cognitive functions

Brandimonte M. A. (2012). *Psicologia della memoria.* Roma: Carocci.

Bruner J. (1986). *Actual minds, possible worlds.* Cambridge, Mass.: Harvard University Press.

Cornoldi C. (2005). *Vizi e virtù della memoria.* Firenze: Giunti.

Gardner H. (1993). *Creating minds.* New York: Basic Books.

Gardner H. (2006). *Multiple intelligences.* New York: Basic Books.

Pascual-Leone J. (1990). Reflections on life-span intelligence, consciousness and ego development. In: C. N. Alexander, E. Langer (Eds.), *Higher stages of human development* (pp. 258–285). Oxford: Oxford University Press.

Piaget J. (1923). *Le langage et la pensée chez l'enfant.* Paris: Delachaux et Niestlé (*The language and thought of the child.* Abingdon: Routledge, 2002).

Piaget J. (1947). *La psychologie de l'intelligence.* Colin: Paris (*The psychology of intelligence.* Abingdon: Routledge, 2001).

Piaget J. (1964). *Six études de psychologie.* Genève: Gonthier.

Schacter D. L. (1966). *Searching for memory. The brain, the mind and the past.* New York: Basic Books.

Sternberg R. (Ed., 1990). *Wisdom. Its nature, origins and development.* Cambridge: Cambridge University Press.

Vygotsky L. S. (1930–1931). Istorija razvitija vyssich psihiseskih funkcij. In: R. V. Rieber (Ed.). *The collected works of L. S. Vygotsky. The history of the development of higher mental functions.* New York: Springer Verlag, 1997.

Vygotsky L. S. (1934). *Myšlenie i reč. Psychologiceskie issledovanija* (*Thought and language*) revised and expanded edition. Cambridge, Mass.; London: MIT Press, 2012.

Vygotsky L. S. (1960). *Razvitie vyssich psihiceskih funkcij.* Moscow: Academy of Pedagogical Sciences of RSFSR.

On health and disease and on some chronic diseases

Antonovsky A. (1979). *Health, stress and coping*. San Francisco: Jossey Bass.

Antonovsky A. (1987). *Unraveling the mystery of health*. San Francisco: Jossey Bass.

Bennett P., Morrison V. (2016). *Introduction to health psychology*. Harlow: Pearson Education Limited.

Bertini M. (2012). *Psicologia della salute*. Milano: Raffaello Cortina.

Bonino S. (Ed., 2013). *Aspetti psicologici nella sclerosi multipla*. Milano: Springer.

French D., Vedhara K., Kaptein A., Weinman J. (2010). *Health psychology*. Oxford: PBS Blackwell.

Lorig K. N., Holman H., Sobel D., Laurent D., Gonzàles V., Minor M. (2000). *Living a healthy life with chronic conditions*. Boulder: Bull.

Ogden J. (2019). *Health psychology*. Buckingham: McGraw-Hill.

Ricci Bitti P. E., Gremigni P. (Eds., 2013). *Psicologia della salute. Modelli teorici e contesti applicativi*. Roma: Carocci.

Ricci Bitti P. E., Candini L., Melani P., Razzaboni E., EduPark Consorzio (Eds., 2006). *Intervento psicoeducativo nella malattia di Parkinson. Il programma EduPark*. Trento: Erickson.

Taylor S. (2018). *Health psychology*. New York: McGraw-Hill Education.

On the functioning of mind, emotions, relations between mind and body and between consciousness and unconsciousness

Bargh J. (2017). *Before you know it. The unconscious reasons we do what we do*. New York: Simon & Schuster.

Battacchi M. W. (2004). *Lo sviluppo emotivo*. Roma-Bari: Laterza.

Biondi M. (1997). *Mente, cervello e sistema immunitario*. Milano: McGraw-Hill.

Blundo C. (2007). *Conoscere e potenziare il cervello*. Firenze: Giunti.

Blundo C. (2011). *Neuroscienze cliniche del comportamento*. Milano: Elsevier.

Borgna E. (2014). *La fragilità che è in noi*. Torino: Einaudi.

Caruana F., Viola M. (2018). *Come funzionano le emozioni*. Bologna: Il Mulino.

Damasio A. (1994). *Descartes' error. Emotion, reason, and the human brain*. New York: Putnam.

Damasio, A. (1999). *The feeling of what happens. Body, emotion and the making of consciousness*. New York: Harcourt Brace.

Edelman G. M. (1987). *Neural Darwinism. The theory of neuronal group selection*. New York: Basic Books.

Edelman G. M. (2004). *Wider than the sky. The phenomenal gift of consciousness*. New Haven: Yale University Press.

Edelman G. M., Tononi G. (2000). *A universe of consciousness*. New York: Basic Books.

Galati, D. (Ed., 1993). *Le emozioni primarie.* Torino: Bollati Boringhieri.

Kihlstrom J. F. (2008). The psychological unconscious. In: L. Pervin, O. John (Eds.), *Handbook of personality* (pp. 593–602). New York: Guilford Press.

LeDoux J. (1996). *The emotional brain. The mysterious underpinnings of emotional life.* New York: Simon and Schuster.

Locke S., Colligan D. (1986). *The healer within. The new medicine of mind and body.* New York: Dutton.

Oliverio A. (2001). *La mente. Istruzioni per l'uso.* Milano: Rizzoli.

Oliverio A. (2002). *Prima lezione di neuroscienze.* Roma-Bari: Laterza.

Panksepp, J. (1998). *Affective neuroscience. The foundation of human and animal emotions.* Oxford: Oxford University Press.

Panksepp, J., Biven, L. (2012). *The archaeology of mind. Neuroevolutionary origins of human emotions.* New York: W. W. Norton.

Rezzonico G. F. A., De Marco A. (2012). *Lavorare con le emozioni nell'approccio costruttivista.* Torino: Bollati Boringhieri.

Strata P. (2014). *La strana coppia. Il rapporto mente-cervello da Cartesio alle neuroscienze.* Roma: Carocci.

Strata P. (2017). *Dormire, forse sognare. Sonno e sogno nelle neuroscienze.* Roma: Carocci.

Umiltà C. (2011). *Il cervello.* Bologna: Il Mulino.

Part II

On identity

Bosma H., Kunnen S. (2001). *Identity and emotion. Development through self-organization.* Cambridge: Cambridge University Press.

Giddens A. (1991). *Modernity and self-identity.* Stanford: Stanford University Press.

Kelleher D., Leavey G. (2004). *Identity and health.* Abingdon: Routledge.

Kroger J. (2000). *Identity development.* Thousand Oaks: Sage.

McLean K. C., Syed M. (2015). *The Oxford handbook of identity development.* Oxford: Oxford University Press.

Oliverio Ferraris A. (2002). *La ricerca dell'identità.* Firenze: Giunti.

Schwartz S. G., Luyckx K., Vignoles V. L. (2011). *Handbook of identity. Theory and research.* New York: Springer.

On search for meaning

Bruner J. S. (1990). *Acts of meaning.* Cambridge, Mass.; London: Harvard University Press.

Frankl V. E. (1946). *Man's search for meaning. An introduction to logotherapy.* Boston: Beacon Press.

Frankl V. E. (1969). *The will to meaning. Foundations and applications of logotherapy.* New York: New American Library.

Frankl V. E. (1997). *Man's search for ultimate meaning.* New York: Perseus Book.

Frankl V. E. (2011). *The unheard cry for meaning. Psychotherapy and humanism.* New York: Simon & Schuster.

On self-efficacy

Bandura A. (Ed., 1995). *Self-efficacy in changing society.* Cambridge: Cambridge University Press.

Bandura A. (1997). *Self-efficacy. The exercise of control.* New York: W. H. Freeman.

Bandura A. (2000). Sviluppo sociale e cognitivo secondo una prospettiva agentica. In: G. V. Caprara and A. Fonzi (Eds.), *L'età sospesa* (pp. 27–58). Firenze: Giunti.

Caprara G. V. (2001). *La valutazione dell'autoefficacia. Costrutti e strumenti.* Trento: Erickson.

On stress, coping, behavioural change, meditation, relaxation, resilience

Astori S. (2017). *Resilienza.* Alba: San Paolo Edizioni.

Beck J. (2011). *Cognitive behavior therapy. Basics and beyond.* New York: Guilford Press.

Beck A. T., Rush A. G., Shaw B. F., Emery G. (1987). *Cognitive therapy of depression.* New York: Guilford Press.

Carosella A., Bottaccioli F. (2012). *Meditazione, psiche e cervello.* Milano: Tecniche Nuove.

Freud A. (2018). *The ego and the mechanisms of defence.* Abingdon: The Hogarth Press.

Frydenberg E. (1997). *Adolescent coping. Theoretical and research perspectives.* London: Routledge.

Goleman D., Davidson R. J. (2017). *Altered traits. Science reveals how meditation changes your mind, brain, and body.* London: Penguin Books.

Kobasa S. C. (1982). The hardy personality: toward a social psychology of stress and health. In: G. S. Sanders, J. Suls (Eds.), *Social psychology of health and illness* (pp. 1–25). Hillsdale: Erlbaum.

Lazarus R. S. (1991). *Emotion and adaptation.* Oxford: Oxford University Press.

Lazarus R. S., Folkman S. (1984). *Stress, appraisal and coping*. New York: Springer.

Miller W. R., Rollnick S. (2012). *Motivational interviewing. Helping people change*. New York: Guilford Press.

Oliverio Ferraris A. (2003). *La forza d'animo*. Milano: Rizzoli.

Rutter M. (1987). Psychosocial resilience and protective mechanisms. *American Journal of Orthopsychiatry*, 57, 316–331.

Schultz J. H. (1934). *Das autogene training*. Leipzig: Thieme.

Selye H. (1956). *The stress of life*. New York: McGraw-Hill.

Siegel D. J. (2007). *The mindful brain. Reflection and attunement in the cultivation of well-being*. New York: W. W. Norton.

Trabucchi P. (2014). *Tecniche di resistenza interiore*. Milano: Mondadori.

Vaillant G. E. (1993). *The wisdom of the ego*. Cambridge, Mass.: Harvard University Press.

Part III

On blaming and guilt

Castelfranchi C., D'Amico R., Poggi I. (Eds., 1994). *Sensi di colpa*. Firenze: Giunti.

Della Seta L. (2010). *Debellare il senso di colpa*. Venezia: Marsilio.

Di Blasio P., Vitali R. (2001). *Sentirsi in colpa*. Bologna: Il Mulino.

Jadoulle V. (2005). *Tout est psychosomatique. Même pas vrai!* Toulouse: Editions Erès.

Lerner M. J. (1980). *The belief in a just world. A fundamental delusion*. New York: Plenum Press.

On depression, learned helplessness, happiness, optimism

Abramson L. Y., Seligman M. E. P., Teasdale J. D. (1978). Learned helplessness in humans. Critique and reformulation. *Journal of Abnormal Psychology*, 87, 49–74.

Anolli L. (2005). *L'ottimismo*. Bologna: Il Mulino.

Argyle M. (1987). *The psychology of happiness*. London: Methuen.

Beck T. (1967). *Depression*. New York: Harper & Row.

Epstein S. (1998). *Constructive thinking. The key to emotional intelligence*. London: Westport.

Goldwurm G. M., Colombo F. (Eds., 2010). *Psicologia positiva*. Trento: Erickson.

Legrenzi P. (1998). *La felicità*. Bologna: Il Mulino.

Seligman M. E. P. (1975). *Helplessness. On depression, development and death*. San Francisco: Freeman.

Seligman M. E. P. (1990). *Learned optimism. How to change your mind and your life*. New York: Pocket Books.

Seligman M. E. P. (2003). The past and future of positive psychology. In: C. L. M. Keyes, J. Haidt (Eds.), *Flourishing. A positive psychology and the life well-lived* (pp. 11–20). Washington, DC: American Psychological Association.

Seligman M. E. P. (2018). *The hope circuit. A psychologist's journey from helplessness to optimism.* New York: Hachette Book Group.

Snyder J., Lopez L. (Eds., 2002). *Handbook of positive psychology.* Oxford: Oxford University Press.

On magic thought

De Martino E. (1948). *Il mondo magico.* Torino: Einaudi.

Fonzi A. (2002). Pensiero magico. In: S. Bonino (Ed.), *Dizionario di psicologia dello sviluppo* (pp. 512–515). Torino: Einaudi.

Fonzi A., Negro Sancipriano E. (1979). *Il mondo magico nel bambino.* Torino: Einaudi.

Odier C. (1966). *L'angoisse et la pensée magique.* Neuchâtel: Delachaux et Niestlé.

Piaget J. (1926) *La représentation du monde chez l'enfant.* Paris: PUF (*The child conception of the world.* London: Routledge & Kegan Paul, 1929).

On narrative thought and story telling

Bert G. (2015). *Medicina narrativa.* Roma: Il Pensiero Scientifico Editore.

Bruner J. S. (1991). La costruzione narrativa della realtà. In: M. Ammaniti, D. Stern (Eds.), *Narrazione e rappresentazione* (pp. 17–42). Roma-Bari: Laterza.

Bruner J. S. (1995). Costruzione del Sé e costruzione del mondo. In: O. Liverta Sempio, A. Marchetti (Eds.), *Il pensiero dell'altro. Contesto, conoscenza e teorie della mente* (pp. 125–137). Milano: Raffaello Cortina.

Bruner J. S. (2009). *Actual minds, possible worlds.* Cambridge, Mass.; London: Harvard University Press.

Charon R. (2007). *Narrative medicine.* Oxford: Oxford University Press.

Demetrio D. (1996). *Raccontarsi. L'autobiografia come cura di sé.* Milano: Raffaello Cortina.

Smorti A. (1994). *Il pensiero narrativo.* Firenze: Giunti.

Smorti A. (Ed., 1997). *Il Sé come testo. Costruzione delle storie e sviluppo della persona.* Firenze: Giunti.

Part IV

On empathy

Bonino S. (2006). Empatia. In: F. Barale, V. Gallese, S. Mistura, A. Zamperini (Eds.), *Dizionario di scienze psicologiche* (pp. 384–386). Torino: Einaudi.

Bonino S., Lo Coco A., Tani F. (1998). *Empatia. Condividere le emozioni.* Firenze: Giunti.

Iacoboni M. (2008). *I neuroni specchio.* Torino: Bollati Boringhieri.

Rizzolatti G., Craighero L. (2004). The mirror-neuron system. *Annual Review of Neuroscience*, 7, 169–192.

Rizzolatti G., Vozza L. (2007). *Nella mente degli altri.* Bologna: Zanichelli.

On trust, therapeutic relationship and its different aspects

Ben Soussan P. (2004). *Le cancer est un combat. Même pas vrai!* Toulouse: Editions Erès.

Benedetti F. (2016). *Il cervello del paziente.* Roma: Fioriti.

Benedetti F. (2018a). *L'effetto placebo.* Roma: Carocci.

Benedetti F. (2018b). *La speranza è un farmaco.* Milano: Mondadori.

Bobbio M. (2017). *Troppa medicina.* Torino: Einaudi.

Caprara G. V. (2006). Disimpegno morale. In: S. Bonino (Ed.), *Dizionario di psicologia dello sviluppo.* (pp. 214–216). Torino: Einaudi.

Cherniss C. (1980). *Staff burnout. Job stress in the human services.* Beverly Hills: Sage.

Crotti N. (1998). *Cancro: percorsi di cura.* Roma: Meltemi.

Donghi P. (1996). *Il sapere della guarigione.* Roma-Bari: Laterza.

Gambetta D. (Ed., 1988). *Trust. Making and breaking cooperative relations.* New York: Blackwell.

Ghirotti G. (1973). *Lungo viaggio nel tunnel della malattia.* Torino: EDA.

Jervis G. (Ed., 1975). *I diritti del malato.* Milano: Feltrinelli.

Jervis G. (2005). *Contro il relativismo.* Roma-Bari: Laterza.

Lemoine P. (1996). *Le mystère du placebo.* Paris: Odile Jacob.

Veronesi U. (2005). *Una carezza per guarire.* Milano: Sperling & Kupfer Editori.

Zamperini A. (1998). *Psicologia sociale della responsabilità.* Torino: UTET.

On different logics, reasoning and decision strategies, heuristics

Battacchi M. W., Battistelli P., Celani G. (1998). *Lo sviluppo del pensiero metarappresentativo e della coscienza.* Milano: Franco Angeli.

Benelli B. (2006). Ragionamento, strategie di. In: S. Bonino (Ed.), *Dizionario di psicologia dello sviluppo* (pp. 578–581). Torino: Einaudi.

Kahneman D. (2011). *Thinking, fast and slow.* New York: Farrar, Straus and Giroux.

Kahneman D., Slovic P., Tversky A. (Eds., 1982). *Judgment under uncertainty. Heuristics and biases.* New York: Cambridge University Press.

Motterlini M., Crupi V. (2005). *Decisioni mediche. Un punto di vista cognitivo.* Milano: Raffaello Cortina.

Rumiati R. (2009). *Decidere.* Bologna: Il Mulino.

On communication

Ekman P. (1973). *Darwin and facial expression. A century of research in review*. New York: Academic Press.
Ekman P. (1985). *Telling lies*. New York: W. W. Norton.
Ekman P., Friesen W. V. (1975). *Unmasking the face. A guide to recognizing emotions from facial cues*. Englewood Cliffs: Prentice Hall.
Watzlawick P., Beavin J., Jackson D. (1967). *Pragmatics of human communication. A study of interactional patterns, pathologies and paradoxes*. New York: W. W. Norton.
Zani B., Selleri P., David D. (Eds., 1996). *La comunicazione. Modelli teorici e contesti sociali*. Roma: Carocci.

Part V

On attachment

Bowlby J. (1969). *Attachment and loss*. Vol. I, *Attachment*. London: Hogarth Press.
Bowlby J. (1988). *A secure base*. London: Routledge.
Zazzo R. (1974). *L'attachement*. Neuchâtel: Delachaux et Niestlé.

On family relations

Gambini P. (2015). *Psicologia della famiglia*. Milano: Angeli.
Scabini E. (1995). *Psicologia sociale della famiglia*. Torino: Boringhieri.
Scabini E., Iafrate R. (2003). *Psicologia dei legami familiari*. Bologna: Il Mulino.

On solitude

Borgna E. (2010). *La solitudine dell'anima*. Milano: Feltrinelli.
Costa E. (Ed., 2000). *Psicopatologia della solitudine. Tra creatività e depressione*. Milano: Guerini.

On cooperation and solidarity

Amerio P., Gattino S. (2000). La solidarietà come risorsa: volontariato e auto-aiuto. In: P. Amerio (Ed.), *Psicologia di comunità* (pp. 389–418). Bologna: Il Mulino.
Bonino S. (2012). *Altruisti per natura*. Roma-Bari: Laterza.
Caprara G. V., Bonino S. (Eds., 2006). *Il comportamento prosociale*. Trento: Erickson.
Eibl-Eibesfeldt I. *Liebe und hass. Zur naturgeschichte elementarer verhaltensweisen*. München: Piper, 1970 (*Love and hate. On the*

natural history of basic behavior patterns. New York: Aldine de Gruyter, 1971).

Jervis G. (2003). *Individualismo e cooperazione*. Roma-Bari: Laterza.

Marta E., Pozzi M. (2007). *Psicologia del volontariato*. Roma: Carocci.

Marta E., Scabini E. (2003). *Giovani volontari*. Firenze: Giunti.

Ranci C. (2006). *Il volontariato*. Bologna: Il Mulino.

Zamperini A. (2001). *Psicologia dell'inerzia e della solidarietà*. Torino: Einaudi.

On death

Campione F., Bandieri E. (2010). *La buona morte*. Bologna: Clueb.

De Angelis M., Trenta P. (2018). *In modo giusto*. Firenze: Emmebi.

Kubler-Ross E. (1969). *On death and dying*. New York: MacMillan.

Morasso G., Invernizzi G. (1989). *Di fronte all'esperienza di morte. Il paziente e i suoi terapeuti*. Milano: Masson.

Spinsanti S. (2017). *Morire in braccio alle grazie*. Roma: Il Pensiero Scientifico Editore.

Testoni I. (2015). *L'ultima nascita*. Torino: Bollati Boringhieri.

Part VI

On communication of diagnosis to children and family life

Nava E., La Porta P. (2018). *Una formidabile gara di ballo*. Milano: Carthusia.

Segal J., Simkins J. (1996). *Helping children with ill or disabled parents*. London: Jessica Kingsley.

On the Internet and social media

Andreoli V. (2018). *Homo stupidus stupidus*. Milano: Rizzoli.

Bonino S. (2018). "Asocial media?" Coinvolgimento, consumo, dipendenza: l'impatto delle nuove tecnologie sulle relazioni. *Quaderni di gruppoanalisi*, 21, 76–92.

Carr N. (2010). *The shallows. What the Internet is doing to our brains*. New York: W. W. Norton.

Lanier J. (2018). *Ten arguments for deleting your social media accounts right now*. London: Bodley Head.

Spitzer M. (2012). *Digitale demenz*. München: Knaur.

Spitzer M. (2018). *Einsamkeit. Die unerkannte Krankheit. Schmerzhaft. Ansteckend. Tödlich*. München: Droemer.

On the mentioned psychological intervention

Bonino S., Graziano F., Borghi M., Marengo D., Molinengo G., Calandri E. (2018). The self-efficacy in Multiple Sclerosis (SEMS) Scale: development and validation with Rasch analysis. *European Journal of Psychological Assessment*, 34 (5), 352–360.

Borghi M., Bonino S., Graziano F., Calandri E. (2018). Exploring change in a group-based psychological intervention for multiple sclerosis patients. *Disability and Rehabilitation*, 40 (14), 1671–1678.

Calandri E., Graziano F., Borghi M., Bonino S. (2016). Depressione e benessere psicologico in persone con sclerosi multipla: il ruolo dell'identità, del senso di coerenza e dell'autoefficacia. *Psicologia della Salute*, 1, 49–66.

Calandri E., Graziano F., Borghi M., Bonino S. (2017a). Improving the quality of life and psychological well-being of recently diagnosed multiple sclerosis patients: preliminary evaluation of a group-based cognitive behavioral intervention. *Disability and Rehabilitation*, 39 (15), 1474–1481.

Calandri E., Graziano F., Borghi M., Bonino S. (2017b). Coping strategies and adjustment to multiple sclerosis among recently diagnosed patients: the mediating role of sense of coherence. *Clinical Rehabilitation*, 31 (10), 1386–1395.

Calandri E., Graziano F., Borghi M., Bonino S. (2018). Depression, positive and negative affect, optimism and health-related quality of life in recently diagnosed multiple sclerosis patients: the role of identity, sense of coherence, and self-efficacy. *Journal of Happiness Studies*, 19 (1), 27–295.

Calandri E., Graziano F., Borghi M., Bonino S. (2019). Young adults' adjustment to a recent diagnosis of multiple sclerosis: the role of identity satisfaction and self-efficacy. *Disability and Health Journal*, 12, 72–78.

Calandri E., Graziano F., Borghi M., Bonino S., Cattelino E. (2020). The role of identity motives on quality of life and depressive symptoms: a comparison between young adults with multiple sclerosis and healthy peers. *Frontiers in Psychology, Developmental Psychology*. https://www.frontiersin.org/journals/psychology.

Graziano F., Calandri E., Borghi M., Bonino S. (2014). The effects of a group-based cognitive behavioral therapy on people with multiple sclerosis: a randomized controlled trial. *Clinical Rehabilitation*, 28, 264–274.

Graziano F., Calandri E., Borghi M., Bonino S. (2020). Adjustment to multiple sclerosis and identity satisfaction among newly diagnosed women: what role does motherhood play? *Women and Health*, 60 (3), 271–283.

Index

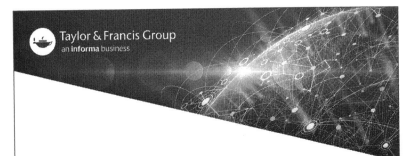